Flowers of Hope

Flowers of Hope

A Memoir
by Victoria Hertig

Momentum Books, Ltd.
Troy, Michigan

1996 © Victoria Hertig

Manufactured in the USA

1998   1997   1996   5   4   3   2   1

Momentum Books, Ltd.
6964 Crooks Road, Suite 1
Troy, Michigan 48098

Cover design by Tim Bodendistel

ISBN: 1-879094-52-5

Library of Congress Cataloging-in-Publication Data
Hertig, Victoria, 1922–
    Flowers of hope : a memoir / by Victoria Hertig.
        p.   cm.
    ISBN 1-879094-52-5 (hardcover : alk. paper)
    1. Hertig, Victoria, 1922– . 2. World War, 1939–1945—Personal
narratives, Polish. 3. World War, 1939–1945—Atrocities. 4. Women—
Poland—Biography. I. Title.
D811.5.H478   1996
940.54'81438—dc20   96-5327

To the American soldiers who liberated me and my family
from the Nazi camps

Acknowledgments

I thank my family for their encouragement.

I thank David S. Molnia for his healthy criticism of my work in his writers club, and Professor Wally Schmidt who listened to my story and advised me to write about it.

I thank Kyle Scott for her enthusiasm and good advice, and most of all my editor Franklin Fox who worked very hard to give my story life.

May God bless all of them.

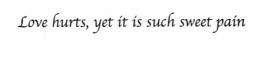

Love hurts, yet it is such sweet pain

PROLOGUE

In 1978 I returned to Poland and visited my town that had died thirty-seven years before. What did I find? Unmarked, forgotten graves and memories that linger with me so clear, as if everything had happened yesterday. As I took pictures, something wrenched in my heart. A tear or two dropped onto the overgrown grass that covers the large mounds beneath which lie the achievements of twisted human minds.

So much time had passed, and so many tears had fallen since I first came here as a child. My mother had met my father during World War I in Hungary where her parents had taken refuge from the Russian Cossacks who had invaded the Carpathian Mountains of what is now Poland. When the Russians left, my parents settled in the city of Krynica. My father was a forest engineer but he lost his job during the great depression and we moved back to the Carpathian Mountains. I was nine when we settled in a small village called Zatwarnica.

My torture began because my parents forced me to marry a man in order to protect the family honor. I was fifteen years old and considered the family disgrace. I hated my husband and was terribly afraid of him. I felt bitterness towards people and God. I found comfort in forbidden love. It was a long time before I found peace.

This is my story.

Chapter One

I came back to Zatwarnica seeking information about those who had lived here before and during the Second World War. News that a strange lady from America had come to the village spread quickly and people came out of their houses to see me, but the strangers who had settled here after the Holocaust had no answers.

An old man approached and tipped his hat.

"Maybe I can help you," he said. "I'm the only one here from the time before the war. I escaped the Ukrainian guerrilla groups, and came back when the bandits left. I found mountains of bodies and the village in ashes. Who are you looking for? Someone important?"

"Very important," I said. "His name is Ivan Fedorchyk. Did you know him?" My heart pounded as I waited for an answer.

"I knew him," the man said. "I knew his family. They are long gone, many of them dead. But Ivan—well, he was also known as Melnik. He was killed here and—" The old man hesitated.

1

"Tell me," I said, paling.

"There is not much to tell except that his grave is over there on that mountain." He pointed. "But who are you, lady?"

"Nobody important," I replied. "Please show me his grave."

The man signaled to a young boy, then sat back and watched us head up the mountain. Half way up, the boy led me to a large umbrella oak with carving on its trunk. I walked up to the tree ever so slowly and stared at the name. *Melnik*. The letters danced before my tear-filled eyes. I stood motionless and read the name over and over again.

"You promised we'd be together forever," I said suddenly, "but you never came back. You didn't keep your promise. Why?"

I bent over the mound of earth at the foot of the tree and cleared away the dry leaves and branches.

"I waited for you all these years," I whispered, harsh sobs beginning to shake my chest. "I looked for you all over the world but never found you. How could I know you were sleeping in this grave?"

I fell to my knees and embraced the cold unmerciful soil that hid beneath it my young love, my dreams, my heart. I closed my eyes and imagined his heart pulsing beneath the cruel earth, saw his blue eyes gazing deeply into mine with so much love. No one could ever smile like him. No one! I could feel again his strong arms around me as he whispered his undying love. And the kiss, his kiss, gentle but fiery.

"My darling, hold me," I said as I had so many years ago. "Never let me go. I want to be with you. Don't send me away."

Though forty years had passed, the memory was as vivid as if I had spoken those words only yesterday. The years meant nothing. They had vanished like snow leaving no trace. Only one day stood between yesterday and today. I was here where I had once lived and loved until the fury of war had torn me from my home, had twisted and broken my heart, and had carried me to an unknown world. Now I had returned to find once more this corner of Poland and the man I loved so dearly. Instead I found his grave.

"I found you, my love!" I said. "You are not dead. What is dead? It is only when one forgets, that one is dead. You are alive in my heart. I can see you and feel you around me. I hear your voice. You are with me. You never left, never!"

"Lady, are you all right?" I heard a young voice inquire. "You've been here a long time."

I climbed slowly to my feet and stared in confusion at the young boy. "Who are you?" I asked haltingly.

The boy responded shyly, "I showed you the way up here, remember?"

Yes, now I remembered.

"I'll be leaving soon," I said. "Wait for me in the village."

The boy ambled off, looking back from time to time at the strange lady from America. I saw a clump of white daisies growing nearby and went to pick some. Ivan had given me daisies when I was sixteen.

"Love me," he had said, "as I will always love you. This tiny white flower will be ours. God knows what war will do to us, and if a time comes that we should be separated, we will have this bond between us. Daisies grow in every corner of this earth. Each time you see one it will remind you of me, and of us. It will hold us together. And if one of us gets lost, we will follow this tiny flower, and it will bring us home."

I placed the tiny white flowers upon the grave and walked back to the village where the car and chauffeur were waiting.

"Where to, Madam?" the chauffeur asked.

I hesitated for a moment. "To Lutowiska," I said.

We drove out of Zatwarnica and crossed the bridge over the River San while I sat silently observing the surrounding country and the gentle slopes of the Carpathian Mountains. Villages disappear. Different people populate the region. Narrow dirt roads have been replaced by good concrete highways. Trees are taller. Meadows are full of colorful flowers. Deer and fox peek from between the branches. It is as it was before, a long time ago when I moved here with my parents, not knowing that my fate was written the first time I set eyes upon the Carpathian Mountains.

The car entered the town of Lutowiska and stopped in front of the Polish Catholic church. I got out and crossed the narrow bridge that separated the church grounds from the street. I wanted to go into the church, but steely shivers grabbed at my spine. I fell back, turned around and looked to my left. There were the graves, fenced by a foot-high chain supported by green and yellow stakes. Inside the enclosed area was a white stone plaque. I moved closer and read the inscription:

Here lie 750 Jewish people,
murdered on June 6, 1942, by —

The rest had been worn off with age. Or perhaps erased purposely. I didn't need an inscription to tell me. I knew. I was here when it had happened. I would have liked to have written their identities on the stone right then but the fear from yesterday was still with me. It would never leave.

I eventually entered the church. Yes, the ghosts were there. I could feel them and hear again their screams. I made a sign of the cross and looked around. The pews were the same, the bullet holes still in them, and the dark patches still on the walls—the blood stains.

I left the church and went back to the fenced grave site where I snapped some pictures. Tears wet my face as I uttered a prayer. Then I got back into the car and left Poland forever. It was summer when I returned to the United States, and the first thing I did was walk into my garden where the white daisies were in bloom.

Chapter Two

March, 1931. The train was speeding, passing telephone poles rapidly. The morning was dark and overcast. A heavy rain mixed with snow was hitting the window panes. While my mother Frances dressed the four younger children, I stood with my small face pressed against the glass and watched the clouds of smoke and red sparks flying by.

Why do we have to move? I wondered to myself as I wiped my tears away. I'm going to miss my friends and my teacher.

A gentle touch startled me. I looked up. My father was standing next to me. He saw my tears and kissed me on the head.

"I know that in the beginning this will be hard for you," he said. "But you're a strong girl. You'll make friends easily, and we'll be living close to your Grandmama and Grandpapa. Their love will make up for your loss."

I pointed to the horizon. "Daddy, look at those tall shadows. They're so scary."

Father came close to the window and peered out.

"They're the Carpathian Mountains," he said. "They look scary now because they're covered with clouds and fog. But on a clear day, and especially in summer, they're the most beautiful mountains in the whole wide world."

I continued to watch the shadows but they didn't seem so scary anymore.

When the train stopped, we could see Grandfather Paff in the crowd at the station. We all waved and he waved back. After hearty hugs and kisses we went to a restaurant for breakfast where we talked, laughed and asked a million questions about our new home.

After breakfast we took our seats in Grandfather Paff's coach and continued our journey through the mountain roads. The trip was long and hard. The rain had soaked the roads, and in some places the deep mud was up to the horses' bellies. It was cold and the coach rolled slowly, but seven hours later we came out of the forest and drove into a town that was nestled in a valley.

Now the rumble of the wheels and the clacking of the horseshoes grew loud as the coach rolled through the cobblestone streets and stopped in the square. The shops were built in a circle around the square. It was still raining so the town looked sleepy and dreary.

"This is Lutowiska," Grandfather Paff said. "It's the oldest town in the heart of the Carpathian Mountains."

"I wonder if it's even on the map," Father said mostly to himself.

Grandfather noticed the discontent on his face.

"Of course it is," he said. "There may not be many people here now, but when it's sunny the town swarms with shoppers and peasants."

"What kind of people are they?" I asked.

"Mostly Poles and Jews," Grandfather said. "The rest is a mixture of Austrians like me, quite a few Ukrainians, and even some Gypsies. We should stop here for dinner while the driver feeds the horses."

A nicely-dressed man came up to us.

"Good day, Von Paff," he said. "What brings you here in such foul weather?"

"Just plain Paff, thank you, Landow," Grandfather said. "My daughter and her family are moving to Zatwarnica from Krynica."

Landow's eyebrows arched.

"From such a beautiful resort city to such a humble village?"

"There's work for me in Zatwarnica," Father said.

"And the finest fresh air in the world," Landow said. "You're sure to like it. My wife and I like it in these parts too, but right now we're very lonely. Our daughter Sheila is away at school. Instead of getting married and blessing us with grandchildren, she's planning to study law. What can you do with a daughter like that?"

"Even so," Grandfather said. "The last time I saw her she was very pretty, and a fine young lady."

"And to help dispel our loneliness you will not eat in a restaurant tonight," Landow said. "You will be our guests."

Grandfather Paff nodded his approval and we all climbed down from the coach and followed Mr. Landow down the street.

"We are very fortunate," Grandfather Paff whispered to me. "As you will see from his house, Landow is a very successful man. He employs only the best craftsmen and produces the best handmade furniture in the region. He also owns a fabric shop and does commerce in the cattle business."

"But why did he call you Von Paff?" I asked.

"That was my name when this land was part of the Austro-Hungarian empire. Now that it's Poland again, my name is just plain Paff. They took away my title, which is no big loss, but they let me keep the estate. For that we can be thankful."

Inside the Landow home it was warm and comfortable. Mrs. Landow was the perfect hostess—friendly, hospitable—a very elegant lady. Two maids served dinner and helped Mother with the children. And while the men talked politics, Mrs. Landow inquired of Mother about fashions in the big city.

"Women!" Landow remarked to the amusement of everybody. "If there were bombs falling a kilometer away they would still be talking about fashions!"

After dinner we said our goodbyes and continued on our journey to Zatwarnica. Mother sank into the back seat and closed her eyes with the younger children cuddled around her. Father leaned quietly back, engrossed in his thoughts, while I rode beside Grandfather.

"Grandfather," I said, breaking the silence. "I like Mr. and Mrs. Landow."

"I like them too," Grandfather said. "The Landows have lived in these mountains since they fled Russia over 150 years ago. Life for them here is a lot more pleasant because we've never taken to persecuting Jews. At least not yet."

Father awakened from his thoughts.

"How much farther?" he asked. "It seems such a long time since we left Lutowiska."

"You're too tired to remember," Grandfather said. "One more curve behind that hill and the bridge will be there."

But when we reached the River San, the bridge wasn't there. The river was full and wild, swollen with the ice that had demolished it.

"My God, what will we do now?" Mother said. "Is there any other way to cross this damned river?"

"Now, now, calm down," Grandfather said. "You grew up here. You know all about this magnificent river."

9

"And each time it comes up this high I am afraid of it!"

"We'll have just to wait until the water recedes," Grandfather said. "Then we can raft across."

"That'll take weeks!"

"Not weeks, my daughter," Grandfather said. "Two or three days and the water level will be back to normal. I know a Jewish family nearby who can give us shelter."

The coach stopped in front of a small house and a short man with a very long beard came out. He recognized Grandfather Paff and took off his hat.

"Good evening, Mr. Paff," he said. "What brings you here so late?"

"Good evening, Mr. Milich," Grandfather said. "I'm in trouble. My daughter and her family are with me and the bridge is gone. Can you put us up?"

"I have a very small house," Mr. Milich said, "and thank God, many children. It may be uncomfortable but you are welcome to stay as long as you have to."

We slept on the straw-covered floor and ate dark bread and warm milk. Milich was a very poor farmer and in the spring food was very scarce. Father wanted to go back to Lutowiska but Grandfather Paff reassured him that the river would recede tomorrow. Tomorrow stretched into three days.

When the river finally cleared of ice, Grandfather Paff paid some peasants from a nearby village to build a raft. The raft looked very uncertain to me and I was frightened of the wild and unruly water. Father took me by the hand and led me to the river's edge where the raft was bouncing in the surging waves.

"The River San looks very angry and I think I know why," he said. "She doesn't want to part with winter. In winter she sleeps in tranquility. When the warm breezes come, the ice breaks and the river has a big job to do. She has to take all this ice down to an even bigger river, the

Wisla, and together they must carry the ice through Krakow and Warsaw to the Baltic Sea. Now do you understand why she looks so scary?"

I gazed at the river with new respect. For the first time I was able to appreciate the awful power and the fierce beauty God had created. Meanwhile, Father and Grandfather climbed aboard the raft and lashed down the luggage.

"We'll cross first and you'll see how easy it is," Father said valiantly.

He sounded fearless but I could tell that in his heart he was worried about his safety and the safety of his family. When the peasant released the rope from the stump, the river swept the raft away with such speed and fury that I quickly lost sight of it. I started to cry, thinking I would never see my father or grandfather again. But soon I saw them waving on the opposite bank and I waved back.

The peasants hauled the raft back and tied us to it. Then they released the rope. The roaring river snatched the raft away quickly and tossed it and its petrified passengers around like a small toy. Mother clutched a rosary to her breast and started to cry. I closed my eyes and held onto the rope tightly, waiting to drown. The younger children screamed as they choked on the brown water that splashed into their faces from the rapids. It seemed that an eternity had passed in those outrageous waves before the raft finally hit something solid. I opened my eyes and saw that we had reached the bank. Father and Grandfather reached out to us and helped us to safety.

The Kopps had arrived in Zatwarnica.

Chapter Three

We came to Grandfather's house exhausted from our ordeal. But the warm house and Grandmother's warm heart healed our frightening experiences. Soon we started to talk and to smile, and after dinner, Ancia the maid took me on a tour.

I marveled at the big kitchen with its large windows, and the dining room that could seat forty people. The sitting room was called a salon, and held many leather-covered sofas and chairs. The walls were covered with paintings and deer antlers. The parquet floors were covered with animal skins of all varieties. It looked more like a hunting lodge than a family room. A large fireplace was built into a corner of the room and the crackling fire was warm and tranquil.

Ancia took me outside and led me up a small hill. From there I could see that the huge white house stood in a valley surrounded by orchards and gardens. Not too far away were smaller houses that Ancia said were for the servants and foremen, and beyond the houses, barns for horses and cattle.

"Ancia, it is really beautiful here," I said. "Just like my Daddy said."

"This is nothing, Miss. Wait until spring when the orchards are in bloom and the gardens shimmer with flowers. Then you'll see the real beauty of this valley. But my village is beautiful too. Look—"

I looked to where Ancia was pointing. The village was indeed beautiful, just like a painting. A small stream flowed through it with a narrow road winding at its side. Farmhouses with straw roofs and attached barns spotted both sides of the stream. In front of the barns were huge mounds that the farmers were digging into with pitchforks and loading onto horse-drawn wagons. When the breeze wafted from that direction it brought the strong odor of manure.

"Your village is very beautiful," I said rubbing my nose. "But it smells."

Ancia laughed.

"To our farmers that is the smell of pure gold," she said. "They have no money to buy fertilizer, so they depend on manure to grow our food."

I looked at the ground, embarrassed at having criticized Ancia's home. Ancia saw my discomfort and gracefully changed the subject.

"Look," she said. "Behind that hill, in the direction of the River San."

"I don't want to," I said. "The river scared me enough."

"Don't look at the river, look at the tall chimneys."

"What's there?"

"The lumber mill, and the apartments of people who work there. I'll take you there tomorrow to meet children of your own age. They're Polish like you. They dress like you and speak your language. In our village, the children speak Ukrainian and dress like me."

I looked to see how Ancia was dressed. She had on a white linen shirt with beautiful embroidery. Her skirt was a brightly-colored floral pattern, and her white half-apron was tied around her waist with a blue ribbon. She had a floral kerchief on her head and homemade moccasins on her feet.

"I like your costume," I said. "It's very attractive. I'm going to learn to speak Ukrainian, and dress just like you."

"No, Miss," Ancia said. "You can learn to speak Ukrainian but you can't dress like we do. Your parents won't permit it."

I wondered why but didn't bother to ask. The day was already filled with too many new experiences.

⊠　　⊠　　⊠

The Kopp family soon settled into a small house on the edge of the estate. Father took an accounting job in the lumber mill and Mother borrowed some land from Grandfather to start a small farm with cows, chickens, geese and pigs. She even planted potatoes, cabbages and other necessary vegetables.

I had just started school when, on the fourth day, a handsome blond boy walked over to me.

"You're new here," he said. "My name is Ivan Fedorchyk. I'm in the sixth grade. What grade are you in?"

"Third," I said. "I'll be in the sixth grade too, in three years."

I turned and walked away, but not too far for he really was good-looking.

"Don't go away," Ivan said following. "I want to be your friend."

Another boy came up and pushed Ivan away.

"She can't be your girlfriend," the boy said to Ivan. "She's Polish and you're Ukrainian."

"Shut up, Zbyshek," Ivan said and punched him on the arm. "You chase all the girls, but you don't even have one girlfriend."

After school I started to walk home with the children who lived in the apartment at the lumber mill. Zbyshek joined us because his father was a plant engineer and that's where he lived. All of a sudden Ivan ran up between us and grabbed my books.

"Let me carry them for you," he said. "It's a whole kilometer to your house."

Zbyshek burst out laughing.

"What's so funny?" I asked.

"Ivan lives in the village," Zbyshek said. "It's in the opposite direction."

Ivan punched Zbyshek again, this time less playfully.

In school I studied Polish and Ukrainian. The latter was permitted by the Polish government because the majority of the people in the Carpathian Mountains were Ukrainians, mostly farmers. They spoke Ukrainian and dressed in their native costumes, the men as colorfully as the women. When they worked the fields they looked like wildflowers in the meadows. I learned that they were very strict with their customs—a sad and romantic people singing beautiful Ukrainian songs. And they were very patriotic, dreaming that one day they would regain their beloved but lost homeland.

Chapter Four

Years passed. It was now 1936 and for the Kopp family, life was unusually quiet. Mother was busy with the children and her small farm. Father was working at the mill. I was fourteen, grown tall and developing into a young woman. Ivan had been sent away to high school, and then to university to study politics. His father was a devoted Ukrainian patriot and wanted his son to follow in his footsteps. Even Zbyshek had gone away to school.

On Easter Sunday I went to church with my family and happened to see Zbyshek who was home for the holidays.

"Ivan is coming home this summer," he said.

I blushed. "So?"

"Want to know something else?"

"What else?" I asked calmly.

"He said he's going to marry you—when you grow up, of course. And he's not going to date other girls because he loves you. Isn't that crazy?"

I turned away, my face as red as a beet.

"I prefer to date a lot of girls," Zbyshek said boastfully. "I've kissed many, and even made love to some of them, one a married woman whose husband works in another town. She made me do things that surprised even me."

I turned away and suddenly ran for home, not waiting for my family to come out of church.

"Ivan is waiting for you!" Zbyshek jeered after me. "Isn't that stupid?"

When I got home I splashed cold water on my face and ran into the forest behind Grandfather's estate. I enjoyed going there alone, especially when distressed. I strolled slowly through the woods and dwelled on what Zbyshek had said.

Ivan said he loves me and would marry me, but I couldn't believe it. He was eighteen and almost a man. I was just a little girl. He'd have to wait for me a long time. No, it wouldn't happen. He'll find an older girl and marry her. But why did he say that to Zbyshek? Maybe he didn't. Maybe Zbyshek was lying. He was known for making things up.

I shook my head to chase the thoughts away and concentrated on the white snow flowers that covered the ground. They looked like brides waiting for their grooms to come and get them. Overhead, the fresh green trees swayed in the light gusts of wind, humming a beautiful melody. Not too far away, a running stream murmured quietly. I picked some of the snow flowers, arranged them in a bouquet and pressed it to my face.

"Ivan, you are coming," I whispered into the flowers. "I haven't seen you for two years and I miss you so!"

My heart started to pound. I didn't know the feeling of love yet but I knew something was happening. Something new and exciting was unfolding within me.

That summer I was in the garden doing my chores when I looked up and saw Ivan standing there. After a moment of fleeting embarrassment I invited him to sit on the bench. He sat beside me, took my hand and kissed it. I looked into his face and smiled, and he smiled back. I was finally able to find words.

"How do you like school in the big city?" I asked haltingly.

"School is fine, we have to study hard," Ivan replied. "But the city is not for me. I miss my village, the mountains, the people. I especially miss you."

I lowered my eyes. I could feel a pink blush veiling my face but I remained in control.

"I miss you too," I said. "I think about you a lot."

"You do?" Ivan's face shone with happiness.

"You're staying through summer, aren't you?"

"Yes and I'll see you again and again if you want me to."

I looked into his eyes. They were blue like the sky.

"Yes," I said. "I want you to."

Ivan smiled, bowed like a gentleman and left. I watched him go and then ran into the house.

"Mommy!" I bubbled. "Guess who I just saw? Ivan's home for the summer! He's grown tall and handsome. Aren't you thrilled that he's back?"

"It's nice that he's home," Mother said kindly. "But I will tell you my child, he's not for you. He's much older, and Ukrainian."

"But Mommy! Everybody in my neighborhood has a beau and now I have one too."

"He's also a peasant. I don't want you to associate with people like that. Find some friends of your own nationality and upbringing."

I didn't answer. Instead, I ran back out to the garden and sat on the bench, sulking.

"What difference is it who he is?" I said to myself as I scuffed the ground. "He's nice, that's what counts. Mother is just old-fashioned. Everything has to be her way. Even Daddy listens to what she says. But I don't have to—and I won't!"

▨ ▨ ▨

That summer I was very happy. Despite what Mother had said, I flirted with Ivan every chance I got. And when September came, he asked me to meet him in the forest behind the plant. I went eagerly, wondering what he had on his mind. He took my hand.

"I asked you to meet me here because I wanted to tell you I love you," he said gravely. "And I want your promise that you won't go out with other boys. I plan to marry you when the time comes."

Before I could respond he took me in his arms and kissed my lips gently. Then he kissed my hand, said a brief goodbye and left. I stood there confused. He hadn't even waited for my promise. He just assumed I would give it. I touched my mouth. I could still feel his lips, and his mustache close to my face—not heavy yet, but there. My first kiss, I thought and put my hand over my pounding heart. I shall never forget it—never, never.

Chapter Five

*I*van left for school in Przemysl. Zbyshek Helder tried to enroll in the University of Krakow but was not accepted. His grades were too poor. He stayed home and took a job at the lumber mill. I finished grade school and my parents sent me to Lutowiska to continue my education and to take singing lessons. Father had high hopes of my becoming an opera singer.

I stayed with Zbyshek's grandmother. His twenty-one-year-old sister was also staying there and Mother thought Janka Helder would be an excellent chaperone. I usually went home on weekends but in winter when the weather was bad I stayed in town and skied with friends. The first year passed uneventfully but it was with great expectations that I returned home for the summer. I knew Ivan was coming home too.

I saw him frequently, but since that first kiss he made no attempt to kiss me again. I had mixed emotions about that. He sat with me in the garden, sang beautiful love songs, but never talked about love. I wondered what was happening. Maybe as he was growing older his feelings for me were fading. If so, why was he so protective of me? When Zbyshek came near me he would get tense as if he wanted to chase him away. Could it be that he was jealous of Zbyshek? If he was, that meant—oh yes!—he still loved me!

I hoped he still loved me, for if he didn't I would have missed him terribly. I didn't yet know why, but when I saw him I felt happy and didn't want him to leave. I could have talked to him endlessly. I liked his smile, and when he looked into my eyes I felt warm all over. My heart pounded very fast. Was that love? Maybe it was. Yes!—I was in love with Ivan! That's what was happening to me! I had discovered a big secret about myself.

⊠　⊠　⊠

In the middle of February my parents were invited to the Grand Winter Ball. With the help of Father, I persuaded Mother to let me attend despite my tender years. Father even slipped me money for a new gown, and Grandfather sent his coachman with a two-horse open sleigh to bring Janka and me home for the gala event.

The day of the ball was bitter cold. A blistering wind whirled around us. We covered our feet with fur blankets and buried ourselves in sheepskin coats until only our eyes and noses showed. We could hardly see the road through the blowing snow but the horses were strong and the coachman knew the way by heart. The ride was smooth and fast, and after an hour the snow stopped. Only the jingling bells of the trotting horses broke the stillness of the winter scene.

We got to our homes before noon so we were able to spend the rest of the day getting ready. As usual, Father was ready first and sat waiting. Mother put on a long black gown and looked striking. I put on my new blue gown and low-heeled pumps. Mother braided my long blonde hair and pinned it high like a golden crown.

"Like a queen," Father said, glowing with admiration. "I'm proud to be escorting two such beautiful women to the grand ball."

When we arrived at the festively decorated hall, the orchestra was playing a Strauss waltz. Like a magic spell, the music enhanced the glamor of the evening. The women were dressed in colorful gowns that shimmered as they swept around the room, and the men all looked especially distinguished in their dark suits and tuxedos.

I sat at a table with my parents and scanned the crowd for familiar faces. Janka was already dancing with a handsome young man. And there, looking unusually tall and slender, was Zbyshek, searching the room with his flashing dark eyes like a young wolf looking for a victim. When he came my way I was positive he was going to ask me to dance. But he only bowed a greeting and went on to ask somebody else. I felt instantly humiliated.

"What if no one asks me to dance?" I pouted.

"Then you shall dance with me," Father said and led us out on the floor for a fox trot.

I was a good dancer and so was Father but I despaired at the idea of having to dance with him all night. After two hours had passed and nobody else asked me, I was sure that would be the dismal case. It was then I saw Ivan approaching and I brightened considerably.

"What are you doing here?" I asked. "Aren't you supposed to be away at school?"

Ivan just grinned. He had no sooner greeted my father and mother than a polka resounded through the hall.

"Mr. Kopp," he said, raising his manly voice above the music and flashing his even white teeth. "May I have this dance with your charming daughter?"

Father nodded graciously and Ivan swung me out onto the floor. My feet hardly touched the ground as he spun me around and around. I tried to look at him but the polka was so fast I wasn't able to see a thing. When the music stopped he swept me back to the table.

I sat down to catch my breath. Ivan turned to Mother and kissed her hand. Then he bowed to Father and said good night. While I watched speechless, he walked across the floor to Zbyshek, said a few words and left the hall.

"Why is he going so soon?" I asked with a pained expression.

"I don't know," Father said, mystified.

"You should both know," Mother said. "He's Ukrainian and wasn't invited. He shouldn't have come in the first place."

"Mother, stop," Father said abruptly. "You always think you're better than other people."

"And you would talk to a Gypsy," Mother said.

To head off the quarrel he knew would ensue, Father led me back onto the dance floor.

"I was hoping Ivan would ask me to dance again," I said. "He's so different from other boys the same age. He's serious and intelligent. Father, why wasn't his family invited to the ball? Because of their social standing?"

"Actually they fit nicely into the community," Father said. "Maybe more so than some of the so-called better class. Ivan's father owns almost as much land as your grandfather. He also owns a mill, so he's quite wealthy and respected."

"Then why? I don't understand."

"He's a Ukrainian politician and patriot. Rumor has it he visited Bandera before Bandera broke out of jail."

"Who's Bandera?"

"Poland's enemy number one. He likes to stir up trouble between us and the Ukrainians. He won't rest until this land belongs to them."

"Would that be so bad?" I asked.

At that moment Zbyshek came over and cut in.

"Ivan asked me to keep you company," he said.

I huffed. "You're dancing with me because it's your duty?"

"Not at all," Zbyshek said. "I enjoy dancing with you, but I like older girls. Besides, you're Ivan's girl and he's my friend. Were you surprised to see him?"

"Yes! He's supposed to be away at school. Why was he here?"

"To see you," Zbyshek said. "He's still crazy."

We were dancing the Krakowiak, a popular Polish dance, and were required to change partners. At the change, I fell into the arms of a strange man who grabbed me and swung me around wildly. He was short and ugly and looked to be in his middle twenties, but he was a good dancer and I knew I would be with him for only a few turns. When the time came to change partners, however, he refused to let me go.

"Sir," I said, "we're supposed to change. Did you forget?"

He laughed, and I could smell the stench of liquor on his breath. I didn't like that but finished the dance anyway. Then to my dismay, he took me back to my parents' table and introduced himself.

"I am Jan Hertig from Lutowiska," he said pompously. "I was invited here by the police chief. He's a good friend of mine."

"And what do you do in Lutowiska, may I ask?" Father inquired.

"I own a tobacco store," he said, all the time looking at me. "It's a good business."

At that moment Janka joined us and snatched Hertig off to dance. I breathed easier.

"What an ugly man," I said. "He keeps watching me."

And sure enough, as soon as Hertig had finished dancing with Janka he came back and insisted I take the floor with him. I did, but only out of politeness. I did not like the man at all. I was relieved when Zbyshek cut in again.

"I'm glad Ivan asked you to keep an eye on me," I said. "That man is disgusting."

"This time it was my sister's idea," Zbyshek said with a wink. "So don't worry about Hertig. She isn't going to let him out of her sight for one minute, at least not tonight."

※　　※　　※

Janka and I snuggled under fur blankets as the sleigh took us back to Lutowiska. Even though my nose and cheeks were red from the cold, I couldn't help but take in the beauty all around us. The mountains and villages were covered with a blanket of white. Little farmhouses with snow-capped straw roofs sat low in the valleys. Wisps of gray smoke spun from their chimneys, attesting that the people inside were warm and comfortable. Occasionally another sleigh passed and the coachmen greeted each other with a nod and a flick of the whip. But mostly there was only brilliant whiteness. A deer paused at the edge of the forest to shake the snow off its back and stare at the passing sleigh, and a pair of foxes jumped playfully into the drifts, digging up the snow with their snouts in a search for mice.

Janka suddenly turned to me.

"I met a very nice man at the ball," she said. "His name is Jan Hertig and he's quite handsome. I think I'm going to give a party one weekend and invite him. He lives in Lutowiska where he owns a tobacco store."

"I know," I said. "If you want my opinion, I think he's ugly and I don't like him. He gave me the shivers when he looked at me."

Janka laughed.

"You don't know anything about men," she said. "You're too innocent and virginal. I know a man when I see one. I want this one, and I will have him."

"Janka, I don't understand the life you lead," I said. "You go out with so many men I can't keep track of them. Now, with this one, you have big plans."

"Yes I have," Janka said smugly.

"I can love only one man," I said. "And I'll be a virgin when he marries me. He'll be mine forever, loving me and only me, and no other woman before me. If he ever cheats on me I'll die."

Janka threw her head back and laughed.

"It's true," I said. "I have a good voice. If I continue my singing lessons, I'll become an opera singer. Then I'll marry Ivan and he'll be so proud of me! Janka, this is my dream and I'll never change it. If God is good to me, it'll all come true."

Janka patted me on the knee.

"Keep dreaming, child," she said.

⁂ ⁂ ⁂

The party Janka planned came all too soon. She arranged it for the last Saturday in February but to her chagrin (and to my relief) a snowstorm struck the night before. We could hear the wind whistling through the house as outside it swirled the snow into huge drifts. No one, I hoped, would come to a party in weather like this. But in the morning the sky was clear and the sun shining. Janka was elated. Even I was delighted when I looked out the window. Fresh snow had covered everything, leaving no sign of life, not even a footstep. It looked like a beautiful wilderness.

I went outside and let the fresh, cold air envelop me. I filled my lungs with it and went back inside to help Janka with preparations for the party. Seven o'clock would come soon enough, and that ugly man would be here in the same house with me. I was very afraid of him and didn't understand why.

Chapter Six

The party got underway and Janka put a stack of records on the phonograph. Fox trots and tangos mingled with the noisy conversation and loud laughter. Janka had the first dance with Jan Hertig. Other guests got up to dance too, but most just sat around consuming liquor and devouring hors d'oeuvres as fast as I brought them in.

I confined myself to the kitchen because the crowd was too old for me, and because that awful man kept staring at me in a way that made me feel uncomfortable. I wanted to get the remaining chores done and go back to my room as soon as possible. I was bending over the sink rinsing the last few glasses when I felt a hand on my shoulder. I stiffened and turned around. Hertig was standing there leering at me.

"You're a pretty little thing," he said, piercing me with his eyes. "I remember you from the ball. Why are you hiding in the kitchen?"

"I'm not hiding," I said. "I'm only helping my friend Janka."

Hertig grasped my chin.

"You're one of those," he said with a smirk. "Untouched by men. Why don't you join us? You'll have more fun out there than you will in here."

I jerked free. "I don't have time for partying. I have to study."

Janka came into the kitchen and took Hertig by the arm.

"What are you doing in here?" she said. "Listen—it's the newest tango. Come dance with me."

Hertig followed Janka out with a backward glance that gave me a chill. I quickly stacked the glasses and slipped out of the kitchen. I could see people in the party room sitting on each other's laps and kissing. It was disgusting. I hurried back to my room, closed the door and tried to lock it but there was no lock. I sat down on the edge of the bed and wrapped my arms tightly around myself. It was getting late. The loud music and the hoarse singing was still echoing through the house. I hoped it would soon stop. I curled up on the bed, drew part of the covers over me and closed my eyes.

I must have fallen asleep for I sat up with a start when I heard the door open and close. Hertig was standing at the foot of my bed, his mouth open in a big grin, his eyes staring unconsciously. He was hopelessly drunk.

"You've lost your way," I said. "The party's in the other end of the house."

"I know where the party is," he said and moved toward me on wobbly legs. "And I know where you are, my little kitten."

I shrank away until I reached the wall.

"Please," I said. "You have no right to be in my room!"

Suddenly he was on me, pressing me against the wall and smearing his wet mouth all over mine. I pushed his drunken face away.

"Get out of here!" I said. "Get out of my room!"

"You don't want it nice, eh? You want it rough?"

"Just please leave! I'm very tired."

"Then we'll go to bed," he said.

He grabbed my braids with one hand and shoved me down on the bed with the other. His breath came in heavy gasps as he pulled my dress open, tore my panties off and slid his hand between my thighs.

"No!" I shouted. "Janka, help! Somebody help me!"

I scratched his face and pulled at his hair but it didn't deter him. He forced his way between my legs and unzipped his pants. Still holding my braids, he maneuvered himself into position and thrust himself into my young virginal body. A horrible groan tore out of my mouth.

"My God, help me!" I cried. "I'm being raped!"

But my cries were drowned in the blasting music and the singing of drunken voices. I was being raped with animal lust, while a roomful of people were singing and dancing in the same house. When he finished his criminal act he stood up and wiped himself on the sheet. Then he straightened his clothes, smoothed his hair and walked out of the room. I lay on the bed trembling, groaning with terror, afraid even to move. Panic started to overwhelm me. I looked up at the picture of Christ on the wall.

"My God," I said. "Why did you let him do this to me? Sweet Jesus, why didn't you protect me?"

I buried my face in the pillow, pulled the covers over my head and broke into a spasm of sobs. It was a long time before the noise of the party finally began to recede and I fell asleep.

Dawn broke gray and ugly. I got out of bed and put on a housecoat. My body ached and my groin was on fire. I walked to the bathroom with great difficulty and washed off the sticky film and blood Hertig had left on me. I was afraid to look in the mirror, afraid to see my abused and shamed body. When I finally did, bitter tears coursed down my cheeks and dropped into the basin.

Was it really me standing there or was it just a bad dream? Jesus, sweet Jesus, please make it a dream. But no, it was no dream. This was my body, destroyed by a bad and mean man. And he'll want to come back and do it again. I had to get dressed and leave that place!

In sudden panic, I rushed back to my room and dressed as quickly as my trembling hands would allow. I put on a coat, drew on my boots and hurried through the house. Janka saw me going out.

"Where are you going in weather like this?"

"Home!" I said without stopping.

"What? Don't be crazy. You'll freeze to death on that road."

"I don't care!" I said and burst out of the house. "I've got to go home!"

I trudged furiously through the deep snow until I reached the road, and then I slowed down to catch my breath. The air was cold on my swollen face, and harsh on my gasping lungs, but I kept on moving. It was a long time before I heard jingling bells and stepped aside to let the sleigh pass.

The coachman drew up alongside me.

"Miss," he asked, "where are you going on a cold day like this?"

"Zatwarnica," I replied through chattering teeth.

"You'll never make it on foot," he said. "I'm going there too. I'll take you."

He helped me into the sleigh. I curled up on the hay and gratefully accepted the sheepskin coat he put over me. The coachman snapped the reins and we started to ride. My face burned from the whipping wind of the open sleigh. I could feel the cold seeping through my entire body. I covered my feet with hay and shoved my hands deeply into my pockets.

"I'd like to make the horses go faster," the coachman said, aware of my discomfort. "But there's too much snow on the road. We should be there in half an hour."

I started weeping quietly so the coachman wouldn't notice. The tears froze on my cheeks.

Half an hour. That meant I would have to face my parents soon. What would I say? I couldn't tell them what Hertig had done to me. There was too much shame in it. What could I say? Why was I coming home?

The coachman pulled up in front of our house.

"I know who lives here," he said. "Von Paff's son-in-law. With all of Paff's coaches and horses, why didn't they send for you in cold weather like this?"

"They didn't know I was coming," I said.

I climbed down from the sleigh and almost fell because my feet were nearly frozen.

"My father will pay you for your kindness," I was able to say.

The coachman waved off the suggestion.

"I don't want to be paid. Just tell him my name is Sabat and he'll know."

He snapped the reins again and drove off while I made my way to the door. I knocked, at first lightly, but no one answered. I knocked again and Father opened the door.

"Victoria!" he said, astounded. "My God, what are you doing here?"

Without waiting for an answer, he led me to a chair in front of the fire.

"Mother, come in here!" he called loudly.

I could feel the warmth enveloping me and grimaced with pain as feeling came back into my hands and feet.

Mother came out of the bedroom.

"What is it?" she said. She saw me huddled before the fire and came quickly to my side. "Victoria! What are you doing home?"

I couldn't answer. I was frightened and confused, and kept rubbing my hands. As they grew warmer the pain grew more severe.

Mother tried to get my attention by shaking me gently.

"Victoria, what happened? Tell me!"

"Not now," Father said. "She's half frozen. She needs something warm to drink."

Mother hesitated, distress filling her eyes, then hurried into the kitchen. Father took off my coat and shoes and rubbed my hands and feet. Soon Mother came back with a glass of warm milk, knelt beside me and held it for me to drink. The warmth penetrated my body and I grew tired and closed my eyes. Father picked me up and carried me into the bedroom where Mother undressed me and covered me with a thick down quilt. When they thought I had fallen asleep, they left the room.

"What terrible thing could have happened that forced her to come home like this?" I heard my mother ask.

"I wish I knew," Father said. "I'm afraid we'll have to wait until tomorrow to find out."

Chapter Seven

*I*n the morning my Mother touched my cheek and called out to my father in alarm.

"Jan, she's burning with fever!" She shook me vigorously. "Child, wake up! Wake up!"

I opened my eyes, looked around dreamily and let out a sharp cry.

"Don't be frightened, sweetheart," Mother said. "Nothing can hurt you now."

I closed my eyes and started to shiver.

"The fever's rising," Mother said. "Quickly, call Dr. Shline. I'll get a cold compress."

When Dr. Shline arrived, he chased my parents out of the room. He examined my neck and throat, and saw something that made him call my parents back in.

"It's a touch of pneumonia," he said. "She's young and strong and should recover completely in a couple of weeks. But I also noticed some bruises on her body, and lacerations on her chin and neck."

"What kind of bruises?" Mother asked.

"I don't know. I need your permission to examine further."

"By all means," I heard Father say, and then I fell back asleep.

❖   ❖   ❖

Three weeks passed and I recovered enough to get out of bed and move around the house. I answered my parents' questions with only the briefest of responses. In what I thought was my private grief, I kept to myself and turned my thoughts inward, dreadful as they were.

Why hadn't I died? What was I going to do now? I couldn't face my parents with the truth, how could I possibly face Ivan? He must never find out what happened to me or he would never want to marry me. I was unclean. My dear God, I was covered with shame. My life was finished!

I sat in a dark corner by the fireplace and sobbed quietly. I hoped my parents wouldn't notice the tears that flowed down my face and fell on my robe, but they did. Mother came over and sat down beside me while Father went outside.

"My child, what's the matter?" she asked. "Why are you crying? Open your heart and tell me all about it. Maybe I can help."

I lifted my tearful eyes to my mother.

"Oh Mommy, Mommy," I said like the little girl I used to be, like the little girl I still wanted to be. "No one can help, and no one can undo it."

Mother held me in her arms.

"Victoria," she said quietly, "your pain is mine, and your daddy's. I know you were hurt by an unscrupulous man, but you must tell me who he is so he can be punished for his crime."

"No, Mommy, no!" I said, suddenly fearful. "No one must know about this! How did you find out? Does Daddy know? I'd die if he found out!"

Mother held my hands tightly.

"Victoria, listen to me," she said. "Daddy and I both know what happened to you. Dr. Shline told us."

I drew back from her and broke into tears.

"Mommy, it was horrible!" I said.

"I know," Mother said soothingly. "We've shared your pain as best as we can, but we must know who the man was. You have to tell us."

I looked at her through wounded eyes.

"Promise you'll never tell anyone," I said. "No matter what."

Mother nodded. "Only your father and I will ever know."

Sobbing uncontrollably, I told her about the frightening ordeal I had suffered that night, that never-to-be-forgotten night that doomed me and changed my life forever.

⸎　⸎　⸎

That evening when Father came home from the office, I stayed in my room. I knew Mother would be telling him about the rape and I couldn't bear to face him. Soon they came into my room and Mother sat next to me so she could hold my hands.

"Victoria," Father said with a quiver in his voice. "Your mother and I have something important to discuss with you."

Mother gripped my hands so tightly I looked to see what was wrong.

"Victoria," Father started again, "we're grieved by the horrible crime Hertig committed against you. So this morning I went and talked to him."

I stared at my father with increasing fear.

"Hertig's very sorry for what he did to you," Father said, his voice breaking. "He asked me to ask you to—marry him."

"Marry him!" I groaned. "Daddy, how could you even think of such a thing? I'm afraid of him! I hate him! He's a brutal, ugly man!"

"We have to think of these things," Father said. "What if he got you pregnant? What then?"

I dropped to my knees and put my head in his lap, sobbing hysterically.

"Daddy, no! Don't do this to me! I beg you!"

"We have to do it this way," he said, choking back his own sorrow. "It's the only honorable solution, for you and for the family. There is no other way, my child. If there was, we'd take it."

He stroked my head.

"This weekend, he'll come to the house and beg your forgiveness," Father said.

"He won't get it!" I shouted.

"I know he won't," Father went on. "But he'll come, and he'll come the weekend after that, and the one after that. And then we'll decide when the wedding will be."

"Please, Father, no!" I cried.

"I told him he would have to take care of you and be good to you for the rest of your life, or I would kill him like the snake that he is," Father said. "It's the only honorable thing to do."

I raised my head and looked at him through eyes brimming with tears.

"I love you very much, Daddy," I said. "I'll do what you ask. But I don't understand why you're punishing me for the crime he committed." I stood up and wiped the tears from my eyes. "May I be excused now?"

Father didn't answer. He couldn't. He had to look away. Mother was crying, and nodded desolately.

I put on my coat and walked out to the cold damp forest. It was still my favorite place. I dropped to the wet ground and cried my heart out. My parents whom I loved dearly had put a sentence on me without pity. To protect the family honor I was going to pay dearly with my life. No one could help me. There was not even anyone to complain to, for no one would be allowed to know my family's terrible secret.

🔳 🔳 🔳

Although my mother's heart wasn't in it, she put on a brave face and went to Lutowiska to shop for my trousseau. She even hinted that a wealthy businessman was courting me and maybe there'd be a wedding soon. And she closed her ears to whispers that Hertig was a known debaucher who spent most of his money on women and liquor.

When Hertig showed up at the house I refused to come out of my room. Mother didn't blame me. She herself could barely look at the man. He was short and stocky with a large nose. Above his thin lips was a long, thin mustache, and his black hair was slicked straight back from his forehead.

Despite Hertig's own feelings of discomfort, he came every weekend as required and sat quietly in the living room with my father. On his third visit, Father told him he would have to ask for my hand on Saturday. We'd have an engagement party soon after, and the wedding would be in June.

Hertig left without a word.

Chapter Eight

*I*n April, Spring unfolded her beauty in the Carpathian Mountains. Mother Earth awakened from her long winter sleep and dressed the fields and meadows in emerald green. In the young green grass, golden dandelions and blue violets opened their sleepy eyes and flirted with the sun's warm rays. Orchards bloomed with white and pink blossoms and filled the air with the sweet aroma of new life. Birds twittered their beautiful melodies as they searched busily for the safest places to build nests for their new families.

Romance was in the air as Spring opened the door to the promise of a joyous new beginning. Peasants plowed their fields with enthusiasm and sowed seeds in the fresh-ly-turned soil in hopes of a harvest of plenty. It was the time of year when excitement and joy embraced all living creatures. From little children to old men, gladness shone in their eyes.

But not in my eyes. Mine were sad and wet with tears. For me this was not the beginning of life and romance. It was the beginning of a frightening new experience. I was getting married to a man who had hurt me, a man I detested, and my young heart ached. I was lost, an innocent victim of my family's pride. I cried and nobody saw. I spoke and nobody heard. I was told the wedding would be in June and that was that. I couldn't understand why I was being punished. I hadn't done anything wrong, yet I was sentenced to marriage for life for a crime someone else had committed against me.

If only I could tell somebody! But that was forbidden by my parents. It was a family secret. I had to live with the pain in my heart and remain mute. So I sat on the bench in the garden where I used to sit with Ivan when he sang songs for me, and I spoke out in the only way I could.

"Ivan, my dear Ivan, I was growing for you," I said to the budding trees and flowers. "You believed in me and loved me so, but I can't marry you now. I'm forced to marry a strange man, a heartless man, a man without honor or conscience, a man I'm afraid of and don't love. I am so alone, and I miss you."

☒　　☒　　☒

When Hertig came to call the first week in May he was disconcerted to find the Kopp house filled with people. My grandmother and grandfather were there as well as my uncles and aunts and friends and neighbors. The table was set for a large party.

"I'm going to make the announcement today," my father told him.

Hertig nodded grimly. "I'll do what you want me to do," he said.

After dinner, to the great surprise of the family and guests, the engagement was announced. Congratulations were given and the party took on momentum that carried it well into the night.

I was crushed at the formal announcement of the wedding date, which was to be the twentieth of May. Forces were being set in motion which would be impossible to stop. When Zbyshek came to pay his compliments, I took him aside.

"Please don't write to Ivan about this," I said. "Don't tell him I'm getting married."

"But Victoria," Zbyshek said. "He'll find out anyway. His father knows and will tell him."

"He won't believe his father. His father doesn't want him to marry a Polish girl so he'll think it's a trick."

Zbyshek was confused.

"You're not happy about this marriage," he said. "Why not? You can tell me, I'm your friend."

"There's nothing to tell," I said. "Honest." I looked at Zbyshek imploringly. "Leave Ivan in peace, at least until the time comes."

* * *

News of the wedding spread from village to village. Everybody who knew the Hertigs, the Kopps and the Paffs began to make preparations, for they knew they would be invited. My girlfriends descended upon me in flocks and regaled me with excitement and curiosity.

"Do you love him?" one asked.

"What a stupid question," I said. "I'm marrying him, aren't I?"

"But you don't seem as excited as you should be. If a man asked me to marry him I'd be terribly excited."

"I thought you and Ivan were close," another asked.

I laughed. "You know he'd never marry me. His father will pick out a nice Ukrainian girl for him."

When I was alone in my room, I allowed myself to think about Jan Hertig. My body shivered. I was afraid of him and the life awaiting me. I felt bitterness toward my father for forcing me into it. I knew Father loved me but he couldn't see how I was suffering. He didn't seem to care what I thought or felt. It was only his will that counted. Oh Daddy, Daddy, couldn't you please change your mind?

But I didn't speak out. My voice wouldn't come.

꙰   ꙰   ꙰

Preparations for the wedding grew hectic. About a hundred people had been invited as well as the entire village of Zatwarnica. Family and guests would dine and dance in Grandfather Paff's house where the wedding celebration would be held. Villagers would dine and dance in the decorated barn.

A week before the event, a butcher came from Lutowiska to prepare two steers, four pigs and hundreds of chickens, ducks and geese. Two cooks were also hired to assist Grandmother Paff's servants with the cooking and baking. And on the Thursday before the wedding, Gypsy musicians were brought from a distant village. They set up on the porch that very night and started to play. It was as if a big holiday was in the offing.

Furniture was removed from the dining room and sitting room and replaced with tables and chairs. White tablecloths were starched and spread, and white lilacs arranged in vases in every room. Their strong and sweet scent permeated the house. By Friday afternoon, guests and family started to arrive, and that evening the first dinner was served. According to tradition it was called Farewell To The Virgin Maiden, and was reserved exclusively for family and close friends. The menu was generous. It consisted of roast beef, pork and poultry, and offered a wide variety of wine and cherry brandy.

The Gypsy orchestra played through dinner and for the dancing that followed. Outside, the night was still, the sky full of silver stars. A big moon smiled down from above. The wind blew softly through the trees and carried to the village the sweet and romantic melodies that emanated from the big house on the hill.

Saturday morning there was a breakfast party but I didn't participate. I slept late. By one o'clock Mother woke me and drew my bath. Afterwards the Maid of Honor arrived with my grandmother and aunts and helped me dress. Grandmama put an egg inside my slip. It fell to the floor and splashed.

"So you will have an easy childbirth," she explained.

The women sang the traditional wedding song that was always sung while the bride was getting ready. They wove herbs into my hair for luck while Mother braided my long tresses and twisted them around my head. Then she placed the veil and decorated it with myrtle.

The bridesmaids giggled as they crowded into the room. They were wearing pink dresses with wreaths of pink flowers in their hair. They presented me a bouquet of white lilacs. I thanked them and went downstairs to where Father was waiting. He took my hand and kissed it.

"You look very pretty," he said. "Like a princess."

He led me to a waiting carriage and four white horses. It too was decorated with white lilacs. Lined up behind it were the coaches of the wedding party, and behind them the musicians who were playing merrily. As soon as my father and I settled in, the horses sprang forward and the carriage started its long journey to the Roman Catholic church in Lutowiska. There was a church in Zatwarnica but it was Greek Catholic and only for Ukrainians.

I sat very still as we rode in the open carriage. I showed no emotion. Under my veil my eyes were dry. In the two and one-half hours it took to reach the church, I never said a word to my father. My mind was far away.

I'll go through with this as you want me to, I was thinking. And I'll be brave. But later I'll show you what I'm going to do.

The church was full. Many people in Lutowiska knew Jan Hertig, and almost everybody knew Grandfather Paff. This was the wedding of the year. Therefore the ceremony was long, too long for me, and I began to grow impatient.

All this praying and speeches by the priests, I thought as I looked at Hertig with his slicked-down hair. If only they knew what had happened and why I was marrying this ugly man. Maybe then they would stop all this praying nonsense and start to curse.

The ceremony eventually ended and the wedding party started for home. Only now I was sitting beside my new husband. We hadn't kissed after the vows, and now we didn't talk. It was a preview of things to come. Hertig finally found the courage to say something.

"You look nice, Victoria."

"Thank you," I answered politely.

Those were the only words we spoke to each other during the long ride back to my grandfather's house. Mother greeted us at the door with bread and salt, an old Polish custom. Grandmother sprinkled us with holy water and invited us into the dining room. We sat down at the center table and the celebration started. Food and liquor flowed profusely, the Gypsy orchestra played brightly, and soon the dancing started. Everybody looked happy, except the bride and groom.

At seven o'clock the villagers came up to the house with their own musicians. They sang loudly, their voices fresh and clear like the streams that flowed through the mountains. Jan Hertig and I went out to accept their congratulations and to catch the flowers that the villagers threw at us.

Grandfather Paff thanked them for their greeting.

"I would invite all of you into the house," he said, "but there isn't enough room. But I'm happy that you came to share in the joy of my granddaughter's wedding, and I'd like you to join me in the barn where there are tables and chairs for everyone, and plenty of food and drink."

He led them to the barn where he drank a toast and, to everyone's delight, joined in the dancing.

Back inside the house, I took a long look around the room. To me it seemed like all the guests were comedians, and I was on the stage. The strange reverie burst when Ivan's father came up to me and took my hand. I felt a cold chill when he kissed it and congratulated me on my good choice of a husband. He was obviously happy that a Polish-Ukrainian union had passed by his son, and now he could find him a wife of his choice.

I thanked Mr. Fedorchyk and looked around for Ivan. I would have liked to have seen him again, but I was glad he wasn't there. Seeing him would have been more than I could bear. And so it was that my heart quickened and then sank when Ivan walked into the room. But instead of coming up to the bridal table, Ivan asked one of the Gypsies for a violin. The music stopped and Ivan stepped forward.

"With your permission," he said to the assembled guests. "I'd like to play a song for the bride."

Everyone applauded and I lowered my head. It looked like the modesty of a young bride, but it was because I dared not look at Ivan.

He started to play, beautifully and with feeling. It was a melody I knew well—a sad, sad love song. I remembered the words.

Hopes are lost, heart is aching,
Tears fill up my eyes.
I loved a girl and that is past,
Heavy is my heart.
If only she knew how true was my love,
She would have loved me too.
With love and devotion
She would have given me her heart.

Ivan finished the melancholy tune and gave the violin back to the Gypsy. Then he melted into the crowd. The orchestra resumed playing and the dancing continued. The sad song was forgotten—by everybody, that is, but me. I could still hear the violin, and the words that it awakened pierced my heart like a knife.

I realized Ivan was saying goodbye, sharing his sorrow with me and throwing his heart at my feet. I stepped on it. I crushed his love and lost him. I married a man I hate. Why didn't I just say no? Why did I go through with this without resistance? Oh my God, what have I done?

I looked around the room again, searching vainly for Ivan. The singing and laughing seemed to grow louder as everybody tried to out-talk one another. Hertig was dancing with Janka who was all over him, making no attempt to hide her amorous feelings. Hertig himself was clearly drunk.

Zbyshek came up to me, took me by the hand and led me away.

"Where are we going?" I asked.

Before he could answer, we entered the hallway. I froze. Ivan was standing there. Zbyshek slipped away and left us alone. Ivan smiled but his face suddenly darkened as if a shadow had fallen over it.

"I planned to spend my life with you," he said. "But you betrayed me without even a word. When I heard you were getting married, anger filled my heart—anger and almost hatred. I began to think that I was a fool for thinking of you as an innocent angel."

I started to say something but Ivan held up his hand.

"I want to give you my wedding wish," he said, coming up and taking my hand. "I am cursing you forever. May you never be happy as long as you live. I hate you and wish you dead."

I snatched back my scalded hand and touched it to my trembling lips.

"I don't hate you," I managed to say. "But I too wish myself dead."

I closed my eyes and fell to the floor. When I came around I was lying on the bridal bed, my mother and father at my side.

"Are you all right, my child?" Mother asked tenderly.

"I'm very tired," I said. "If I can just rest a while."

"You've had a long day," Father said. "We'll say good night to our guests for you."

I waited until Mother and Father closed the door before I burst out crying. I had been holding on, playing a role all day, but now my body and heart exploded and all the hurt came rushing out. I didn't go back downstairs. I couldn't. It was all I could do to wait in this room for what was inevitable.

It was very late when Hertig came up, but still too soon for me. I listened to him stagger around the room in a drunken stupor, mumbling loudly and incoherently. He bumped into the bed and fell across it. He grabbed at me and tried to kiss me but I pushed him away. That seemed to be what he was waiting for, for his animal instinct became aroused.

"You're my wife now," he growled. "I can have you as much as I want and you can't say no. But this time I want you to enjoy it."

He threw himself on top of me and groped my body with his brutal hands. I lay still, petrified with fear, not knowing what to do. I couldn't scream because people would hear. I could only endure.

"It's not working for me," he said after some awkward effort. "You can't just lie there like that. You're supposed to help."

"You're hurting me," I said. "Please stop. I can't stand the pain."

"Not until I finish!"

He continued to force himself on me but with diminishing passion. Finally he stopped and rested on top of me. I waited for him to roll away but he began to snore. He had fallen asleep. I eased out from under him and crawled out of bed. My body burned with pain, and my gown was stained. I stared at myself in the mirror. I looked like a used rag. It would take weeks for my body to heal.

I washed off the blood, put on a clean gown and carefully got back into bed so as not to disturb him. It was not until morning that he attempted to finish what he had failed to accomplish the night before. Again I pushed him away.

"I'm your husband," he said. "I have rights."

He forced himself on me, only this time my torture was brief. He finished quickly, groaned and rolled to one side. I left the cursed bed and scrubbed myself clean once more. It was disgusting and painful and I hated him even more than I already did.

If it's going to be like this every night, I'd rather die, I said to myself. I won't go with him. If they force me to, I'll jump off the bridge and drown.

The wedding festivities were far from over. The going-away party lasted all day Sunday and continued into the night. I walked through it in a trance, reluctant to go to bed even though my body ached. I finally succumbed to fatigue and went upstairs. I climbed into the hated bridal bed and fell asleep as soon as my head touched the pillow. To my relief it turned out to be a tranquil night. Hertig had not come to bed at all.

In the morning I found Hertig in one of the rooms downstairs. He was sleeping on a couch. Disgust welled up inside me as I stared down at his slovenly shape.

"He was too tipsy to go upstairs," Mother said when she came into the room. "So we left him here." She looked at my dressing gown. "You'd better get ready. As soon as your husband wakes up, you can leave."

"I'm not going anywhere," I said.

"But all your things are packed. Grandfather has even provided an extra coach for your wedding presents."

"Mother, I don't want this man," I said firmly. "I don't like what he's doing to me and will not be married to him. If you make me go, I'll kill myself."

"Don't be ridiculous," Mother said. "He's your husband. Now do as I say and get ready."

"You can't tell me what to do any longer," I said. "I'm Mrs. Hertig now, remember? I can do as I please."

"You'll do what you're told!" Mother said sternly.

"I will not!" I said. "Or shall I tell Grandpapa why I was married off to that man?"

I ran back to my room and refused to come out even after Jan Hertig had pulled himself together and stood waiting by the coach. He finally left with my trousseau and dowry. He appeared not to be too upset at having to leave without his young wife. My dowry was generous not only in goods but in money I had received from my father and grandfather. That apparently made up for a lot.

Chapter Nine

Mother was mad at me for talking back to her and for the embarrassing stunt I had pulled.

"What are we going to do with her?" I overheard her ask my father. "If she doesn't go live with her husband, we'll be the joke of the community."

"Don't rush her," my father said. "Give her time to rest up and get used to this great change in her life. And let's not forget the traumatic experience she went through. We should let her make her own decisions for a change."

For my part I was glad the comedy of my wedding was over and I didn't have to see Jan Hertig again. I felt free for the first time in a long time. I wanted to see Ivan but I knew he was probably back at school and wouldn't want to see me in any case. On one of my long walks I ran into Zbyshek. He presented me with the first laugh I'd had in a long time. He was limping down the road with his legs held wide apart.

"What happened?" I asked. "You can hardly walk."

"You know that affair I was having with a married woman?" Zbyshek said. "Well her husband came home unexpectedly and she practically threw me and my clothes off her balcony."

I laughed. "The price you pay for fooling around with married women."

"It's not funny. I had to crouch naked in the nettle and listen to her say she was out on the balcony with no clothes on because she was pining for him. The jerk fell for it."

"Zbyshek, you're such a great lover, why don't you find a girl your own age? One without a husband?"

"Young girls get pregnant" Zbyshek said. "An older woman with a stupid husband is safer. It makes a big difference."

I watched him walk away with his legs still wide apart and tried to stifle my laughter. When Zbyshek turned around I wiped the grin from my face.

"You won't tell anyone, will you?" he asked.

"Promise," I said. "Besides, who'd believe it?"

"I know," Zbyshek said. "Even I don't believe it."

◆　◆　◆

A month passed. I regained my strength and the roses returned to my cheeks. I had finally begun to make peace with myself and was even starting to accept my fate. I had lost Ivan, I decided on another of my long walks in the woods. He was going to forget me and erase me forever from his heart. Oh Ivan, Ivan! If he only knew how much I missed him and loved him! But he didn't know and never would—the tragedy of my life.

For the first time I was able to chase these melancholy thoughts away and lock my sorrow deep in my heart. I was beginning to realize that I too had a duty to protect my family's dignity and reputation—a role to play and it had to be played well. In some ways Father had been right. He was being very tolerant in letting me come to this understanding on my own.

I went to Grandfather's estate and asked him if he could send a carriage to take me to Lutowiska in the morning.

"Of course, child, but why?" Grandfather asked.

"I have to go to my husband and start my life as a married woman," I said.

"Is your father or mother going with you?"

"I don't want them to," I said. "They still don't know that I've decided to go."

"Then I'll take you. I don't want you going alone."

"Thank you, Grandpapa, but I have to do this myself. I'm a grown and married woman. It's time for me to make my own decisions, don't you think?"

Grandfather Paff looked down at me.

"You're right," he said. "And as soon as you're settled in your new home we'll come visit you." He stroked my head. "Good luck to you, my child. I shall miss you."

"I shall miss you too, Grandpapa."

That evening I locked myself in my room and packed everything that belonged to me. Putting away my precious souvenirs stirred memories of when I was a little girl. The days were all so happy and carefree then but now I was on my own. I had to be strong and brave, for tomorrow I would start a new life.

Early the next morning the carriage pulled up in front of the house and Father stared at it with curiosity.

"What's that for?" he asked.

I came out of my room carrying a suitcase.

"Goodbye mother, goodbye father," I said and kissed them both.

"Where are you going?" Mother asked.

"To Lutowiska," I said. "I love you and will miss you, but it's time for me to leave my home."

I walked out to the carriage, climbed on board and was on my way before my flabbergasted parents could say anything else.

※　　※　　※

A somewhat surprised Jan Hertig saw the carriage pull up and watched me get out. He hurried to it, greeted me rather awkwardly, and took my suitcase. I looked around as we walked up to the house. On each side there was an attractive flower garden, and just visible in back, a neat vegetable garden. We went inside and an older woman came up to me. She curtsied and flashed a friendly smile.

"This is Petrusia," Hertig said. "She manages the house for me and my brother Edward."

"Welcome, mistress," Petrusia said. "I try to do everything as best as I know how, but you're the lady of the house. If you want any changes, I'll do as you wish."

"Thank you," I said, "but everything looks all right to me."

A new chapter had started in my life. I was now a married woman and was beginning to act like one.

"I shall help you unpack," Petrusia said and took the suitcase from a still dumbfounded Hertig.

"Let me show you around first," Hertig said and led me into the sitting room.

I noticed my suitcases and trunks standing unopened in the corner.

"The house looks very comfortable," I said.

Hertig's brother came out of his room and introduced himself. He was slightly younger and a good deal more handsome.

"Eddie's no trouble," Hertig said. "We have six large rooms plus a kitchen and bathroom, with installed water and plumbing. Not as grand as the Von Paff estate, but we're in a nice section of town."

"It'll do nicely," I said.

I looked out the front window.

"That's the courthouse across the street," Edward said. "You'll be able to sit on the veranda and watch all the important comings and goings."

"I won't have time," I said.

"Why not?" Jan Hertig asked.

"You have a tobacco store, don't you? I'm sure you can use all the help you can get."

Hertig smiled weakly and Edward winked at him.

"I certainly can," Hertig said without enthusiasm.

I proved to be quite a good saleslady and Hertig was pleased. He began to be much nicer to me, and I started calling him Jan even though at first it was difficult for me to refer to him by my father's name. Our sex life, on the other hand, remained as grim as ever. I got used to this wifely duty, and for me it remained a duty. I never achieved satisfaction, which was of no importance. It was evidently a service men required and it was they who had to be satisfied. Since it no longer caused me pain, it no longer bothered me when he made love to me. My body was getting used to it.

But it started to bother Jan. He appeared to be falling in love with me and kept trying to arouse me. It never seemed to work. In frustration he told me I was like a cold fish. At the time, I didn't understand what he was talking about. I was doing my job, wasn't I?

Petrusia took care of the house so I didn't have to worry about cooking, cleaning or washing. This gave me lots of time for myself after the store closed. I started to dress better, like my mother did, and I started to feel better.

I would wander into the garden and think about Ivan. I was trying hard to forget him yet somehow his face was always before me. It was at moments like this that I grew very quiet and retreated into myself.

※　　※　　※

I had already become acquainted with quite a few people in Lutowiska. But one afternoon, one of the most interesting and beautiful women I would ever meet came knocking on my door. Her long black hair and expressive black eyes contrasted sharply with her smart white suit.

"I'm Sheila Landow," she said. "My father's a good friend of your grandfather and told me to welcome you. You're new in town and so very young, maybe I can help. I'd like to be your friend."

"I'd like to be your friend too," I said happily. "Your father and mother had us to dinner when we were moving to Zatwarnica. I shall always be in their debt. Come in and we'll have tea."

As Sheila and I talked, Petrusia brought in tea and warm biscuits. Sheila told me she was a law student home on summer vacation.

"We're having a dance at our club on Saturday," she said. "I'd like you and your husband to be my guests."

"We'd love to," I said. "I've been to only one dance, and since then I haven't been anywhere except to my own wedding."

"Then you'll enjoy it." Sheila looked down into her cup with visible embarrassment. "I have another reason for asking," she said. "I mean besides really wanting you to come, which I sincerely do."

I cocked my head and Sheila cast her eyes about the house.

"I'd like you to bring Edward," she said quietly. "I've met him before, but I'd like to know him better."

I smiled at this polished and sophisticated lady who was suddenly acting like a school girl.

"Wild horses won't keep him away when he learns he got a special invitation from you," I said.

"No, no!" Sheila said getting up to go. "Just make it sound casual. I wouldn't want him to think I'm after him."

"Aren't you?" I asked boldly.

Sheila just smiled. "See you next week." She glided out the door as elegantly as she had come in.

I watched her walk across the street to the courthouse. I was glad she wanted to be my friend even though it may have been to get closer to Edward. That was of no consequence. Sheila was everything I had always wanted to be, and her life still lay ahead of her.

At dinner that evening I told Jan and Edward about Sheila Landow's visit. I tried to be nonchalant about the invitation.

"I know why she came," Edward said. "She's after me, isn't she?"

"You think you're some kind of Don Juan?" Jan scoffed. "Every guy in town is after her, and you think she's after you? I'll bet she doesn't even know you exist."

"I'll bet she does," Edward said. "She came into the store last week and our eyes made contact."

"Made contact?" Jan said. "What's that supposed to mean? You pulled one of your eyeballs out of its socket and rubbed it against one of hers? Like billiard balls?"

"It means her eyes are a beautiful deep brown," Edward said staring off into the distance.

"If you don't want to go," I said coyly, "I can always tell her we have other plans."

"No, no, no!" Edward said quickly. "Don't tell her that."

"Don't tell her anything," Jan said. "I still haven't decided whether we're going at all."

I watched Jan as he turned his attention to his plate. I'm young and haven't lived, I wanted to say to him while he stuffed mashed potatoes into his mouth. I need to go out and make new friends. Maybe it'll help me forget Ivan, my loveless marriage and you! But I said nothing.

When at last Jan decided we would go, I bought a new dress. I liked what I saw in the mirror. Jan didn't look too bad either in his gray suit. If only he was a little taller. Edward was much taller. With his blond hair and blue eyes he looked quite handsome in his dark suit. No wonder Sheila Landow was interested in him.

As we walked to the club we could hear the music playing. It was a beautiful July evening, warm and quiet. The scent of flowers from the valley filled the air and mingled with the rich aroma of freshly drying hay. Sheila was standing at the door of the club, nervously clutching her purse. She had on a long black dress with a gold and diamond brooch pinned on her shoulder. With her hair pinned up she looked stunning.

We exchanged greetings but it was immediately obvious that Sheila and Edward only had eyes for each other. With hardly another word they went off to the dance floor and sailed into a tango.

"That's the last we'll see of Don Juan," Jan said.

And that seemed to be the case. Even though Jan and I stayed until after midnight and left only because I felt sick to my stomach, Edward and Sheila remained glued to the dance floor, and to each other.

Three days later Edward stopped me on my way to the shop.

"Today's my day off," he said privately. "I wonder if you could find something for Petrusia to do this afternoon, outside the house."

At first I was baffled by his request but then I quickly caught on.

"You mean like visit her mother on the farm?" I asked.

"At least until dinner."

I winked. "I think she'll be delighted to have the afternoon to herself."

I informed Petrusia and then left for the shop. At the corner I paused to look back at the house. I saw Petrusia leave by the back door. Across the street, in the doorway of the courthouse, I could see Sheila Landow waiting. I smiled to myself and walked on, not daring to imagine what ecstasy awaited them. It would only make me think of Ivan and I didn't want to do that anymore.

▨　　▨　　▨

After their afternoon of passionate lovemaking, Sheila and Eddie started dating secretly. At least they thought it was secret. Somehow the rumor flashed through Lutowiska, and their clandestine romance was on everybody's lips. Jan heard it from a customer but refused to comment. However, he did begin to notice Edward's repeated requests for afternoons off. He finally confronted Edward in the back room. Even though they spoke in hushed tones I heard everything they said.

"The whole town's talking about you and Sheila Landow," Jan said. "What's going on?"

"This is not the town's business," Edward said. "Or yours."

"But Eddie, she's Jewish. You have no chance. You know how strict they are about allowing their children to mix with Catholics. And I don't think you're ready to wear a yarmulke."

"Look," Edward said abruptly. "I love her and she loves me, and no one can change that. Not you, not her father, not a hundred priests or a thousand rabbis, not even God himself. This is our life and our destiny." He paused and added softly, "I'm going to marry her."

"Eddie, come to your senses," Jan said. "Her family's very religious. They'll never allow you to do something as stupid as that."

"Stupid?" Edward said angrily. "Stupid for you because you don't know what love is. You don't love Victoria, and you didn't marry her for love. You hurt her and now you're both suffering. So don't talk to me about love."

"I like Sheila," Jan said, "and I respect your feelings. But I think you should take it easy. There's lots of time."

"You don't understand how I feel," Edward said. "If I have to convert to Judaism to marry her, that's what I'll do. And I'll get permission from her father too. You'll see."

Chapter Ten

*W*ith mixed emotions, I wrote my parents and told them I was going to have a baby. From the letter I received back from Father, I could tell Mother clearly wasn't happy. She felt she was much too young to be a grandmother. But Father was delighted because it proved Jan and I were finally living together as man and wife. I smiled to myself and continued reading Father's letter:

Uncle Leon stopped by and also extends his congratulations. He's glad our family is growing in spite of the threat of war. He had just heard on the radio that the Germans were confiscating everything owned by Jews and moving the Jews into camps.

Mr. Adlesberg, owner of the factory where I work, just came back from Germany on business. He confirms that it's very bad there for Jews. He felt uncomfortable all the while because he's Jewish and was afraid something would happen to him. Nevertheless we continue to do business with the Germans, selling them rifle stocks. Business is business, Mr. Adlesberg says. He hopes nothing will happen. Sometimes from a big cloud there's very little rain. He would like to keep his factory running so his employees can make a living. I happen to think he's right. The depression is severe in Poland. People go from village to village looking for work, but here in Zatwarnica we still have our jobs.

Your Uncle Leon also says the Germans aren't our only enemies. A man who works in his lumberyard came into his office and started a fight with him, if you can believe it. He said he hates management, and that when the war comes and the Russians take over, Uncle Leon will be hanged from the rafters by the working people. He said Uncle Leon may be a big shot now, but soon his reign will be over. I told your uncle that the man is surely a Communist and should be arrested. But your uncle was typically reluctant. He said the man's wife, whom he beats every day, and his five children will starve. He wouldn't have the heart to turn him in. So he lets him bark. He says the Russians are still far away.

I folded the letter, leaned back in my rocking chair and closed my eyes. How beautiful and peaceful this part of the world is, and yet who knows what evil is awaiting it.

▩ ▩ ▩

I was alone in the shop when Zbyshek came in unexpectedly.

"What are you doing in Lutowiska?" I asked happily. "Did you come all this way just to buy cigarettes?"

"I have something important to tell you," he said solemnly. "Ivan's home on vacation."

I brightened momentarily but then adopted an aloof air.

"That's not important," I said. "After all it is summer. But how's your love life, Zbyshek? Outrageous as ever?"

Zbyshek groaned. "I'm in love with the woman I'm having an affair with."

"What's wrong with that?"

"Plenty. If I thought one day she would say this is the end of the affair, I would die—that's how much I love her. Yet she's at home, probably making love with her husband, while I stand watching her window like a hungry dog. It's outrageous, all right, but that's not what I came to tell you."

"What did you come to tell me?"

Zbyshek looked around to make sure we were alone.

"The other day I went to visit Ivan," he said, "but his sister wouldn't let me in the house. There was a big meeting going on and she didn't think her father would want me around. That really surprised me. They never treated me like that before. So I went around back to peek through the window."

"Zbyshek!" I scolded. "You didn't!"

"It must have been a very secret meeting because Ivan's father had lowered all the shades and sent men outside to guard the house. But I was able to hide in the bushes and see through a crack."

"What did you see?"

"Men inside from other villages, and somebody called Hoculak from the Ukraine. Now what do you suppose a man from the Ukraine is doing in Zatwarnica?"

"I don't have the faintest idea," I said.

"Well I do," Zbyshek said. "Especially after Hoculak said Bandera was in Berlin, making a deal with Hitler."

"I heard that Bandera escaped from prison," I said trying to act informed. "But nobody knows what happened to him. What kind of a deal could he be making?"

"I had to beat it out of there before I found out," Zbyshek said, "but I can guess. The Ukrainians are having these meetings in every village in the Carpathians. They're saying that when the Germans invade Poland, they'll create an independent state for them. That's what the deal is all about. Can you believe it? We're not even at war and already our country's being divided up by our enemies. It makes me sick. It should make you sick too, however much you care for Ivan."

"Why doesn't our government do something?" I asked, shifting the subject away from Ivan. "They must know about these things."

"If they don't, then we're really in trouble."

"What will happen to us if the Germans invade?"

"We'll fight like hell," Zbyshek said. "We've got the finest cavalry in Europe, maybe the best soldiers, too. And we have great spirit and unity. At least I used to think so. But now it looks like we can't count on our Ukrainian friends."

I put on a serious face but all I could think of was Ivan and how much I missed spending the summer with him.

Chapter Eleven

*I*n Lutowiska, a special market day called *Jarmark* came twice a year, once in the spring and once in the fall. In the spring, farmers would bring to market goods they made during the winter—hand-woven linen, embroidered tablecloths, sheepskin jackets, carved and painted wooden plates, barrels, and even carriages and wagons. In return they would buy farm equipment, fabrics, ribbons and candles, salt and kerosene, shoes, candy, sugar, and whiskey. The wealthier farmers would also buy fertilizer.

But in the fall, *Jarmark* was reserved for cattle raised by the Ukrainians who lived in the mountains where the land was good but not good enough to plow. The lifestyle of these mountain people was primitive. They lived in small houses with straw-covered roofs and dirt floors. They were self-sufficient and produced their own clothing and food. Their diet consisted mainly of potatoes and sauerkraut sprinkled with pork fat, dark bread, milk, cheese, butter and eggs. Coffee and sugar were for holidays, and meat was for Sundays. They lived long, healthy lives and seldom saw a doctor. They were also the largest producers of cattle in Poland, and businessmen came from all over Europe to buy their beef.

After *Jarmark* everybody was always happy. Businessmen made money, peasants made money, even Jan's tobacco store made more money than usual. The Gypsies also made money reading cards and telling fortunes. But this year that made Edward unhappy.

"What's wrong, Eddie?" I asked as we were closing up shop. "You look like you just lost your best friend."

"I may have," Edward said. "A Gypsy woman insisted on reading my palm, and when I let her, she didn't like what she saw."

"What did she see?"

"Two broken hearts. Parted and never to come together again. For me, a long journey and then imprisonment. Hard work and then blood. But not my blood. Isn't that odd?"

"That's awful," I said. "Did she tell you anything good for your money?"

"She said my heart will ache for a very long time."

"That isn't so good," I said.

Edward suddenly laughed. "I've just received my draft notice. That's sure to involve a journey and lots of hard work."

"And Sheila's gone back to law school," I said. "So there's your parting. But I don't believe for a minute that you'll never see each other again. You're too much in love."

"That's the part that worries me," Edward said. "Sheila had the same premonition the Gypsy did." He shuddered. "So did I. But I promised Sheila that we'd see each other at Christmas, no matter what."

"Not many people find true and lasting love," I said. "I hope you have, and that you and Sheila will be together forever and never taste the bitterness and disillusionment of losing each other."

Edward smiled and looked down at his palm.

"Whose blood do you think the Gypsy saw?" he asked. "She didn't say, and I forgot to ask."

The next afternoon was quiet in the shop so I went for a walk in the fields. Most of the crops had been harvested, but the farmers were still hoeing potatoes out of the ground. I watched them as they bent over, their hands chapped and red, and scooped the potatoes into baskets. They wasted no time talking or looking up. Potatoes had to be taken before the first frost or be lost, and they couldn't afford to lose them. This was their basic food. When full, the baskets were emptied into sacks. The sacks were hauled to horse-drawn wagons and piled so high they looked like they would topple over.

Occasionally the farmers walked to the small fires that flickered in the field and warmed their hands. With long sticks they turned the potatoes that were baking in the coals, and then gathered around the fire to eat them with flasks of cold milk. The cool breeze scattered sparks from the fires and carried with it the aroma of baked potatoes, a reminder of fall and the winter that was coming.

"Oh how I love fall!" I said to myself, doing a little turn. "But why? It doesn't have beauty like spring or summer. Yet there's something special about it. I know! Fall has loneliness, melancholy and longing for something that is lost."

I looked in the direction of my home—my parents' home—and wondered what Ivan was doing. Was he as lonely as I was? Maybe he'd forgotten all about me and found somebody new. My darling Ivan! If he only knew how much I missed him!

Chapter Twelve

$\mathcal{B}$y the end of October I was feeling extremely lonely. Sheila was away at law school, Edward was off in the army, and Jan wasn't interested in talking to me about anything but the shop, or to give me orders. Zbyshek was the only person who had ever talked to me about what was happening in the world, and he lived in Zatwarnica.

I was therefore delighted when I went to order winter boots and Mr. Friedes told me his wife was anxious to meet me. So that same evening I walked the short distance to the Friedes house. As I drew near, my attention turned to the window. It was shaded with fine lace. Through it I could see Mr. Friedes looking very dignified, sitting at the head of a table covered with white linen. He was holding a big black book and swaying slowly back and forth, his lips moving in a prayer. Mrs. Friedes, a black lace shawl over her head, was standing by the lighted candles. The children were sitting on each side of the table with bowed heads, listening to their father.

There is God and love in this house, I thought. In this house there is peace.

I realized I was intruding and felt suddenly ashamed. Since it would have been rude to interrupt their supper, I continued walking through the neighborhood. By the time I returned I had passed many windows with scenes similar to the one in the Friedes home—all with God and love in them.

"*Guten Shabbas*," Mr. Friedes said when he opened the door for me. "Good Sabbath."

I remembered it was Friday and past sundown, the beginning of the Jewish Sabbath.

"*Guten Shabbas*," I replied.

"Come in and meet my family," Mr. Friedes said warmly and led me into the parlor. "Sarah, children, I'd like you to meet Mrs. Hertig, our charming new neighbor."

We chatted over tea and poppy strudel until late into the evening, and when I got home I told Jan and Petrusia about my pleasant visit.

"They're Jews," Jan said bluntly. "Just like the Landows."

I looked at Petrusia to see if there was some significance in his remark but Petrusia just shrugged.

"They're very nice people too," I said. "Just like the Landows."

In the middle of November a white dusting of snow covered the ground. Animals slinked deep into the forest to hide from winter's cold winds. Birds and wild geese left the mountains to fly south, leaving their courageous cousins behind. The sparrows and crows flew over the empty fields and fed on what few spilled oats they could find. Stillness covered the earth. All signs pointed to a hard winter to come.

Zbyshek popped into the shop again after lurking across the street to make sure I was alone.

"What's all this furtiveness?" I asked.

"Everybody's talking about how pregnant you are," he said. "I came to see for myself."

"Then see," I said and came out from behind the counter. I did an awkward twirl and together we laughed.

"I wonder what Ivan will say when he finds out?" Zbyshek said.

"Ivan," I repeated like an echo, my smile fading. "He must be back at school. How is he, Zbyshek?"

"I don't know," Zbyshek said, growing serious. "He doesn't answer my letters. I thought maybe he was writing to you."

"Never," I said.

"His father says he's not coming home for Christmas because he's got a lot of studying to do, but that's not like Ivan. There must be another reason."

"Maybe he's found a new love."

"I doubt it," Zbyshek said, watching my eyes as he talked. "Do you miss him? If you do I understand."

I turned my face away.

"Of course I don't miss him," I said. "I'm married. You shouldn't ask questions like that."

"I guess I shouldn't," Zbyshek said. "I miss him. I'd like to know what happened to the Ivan I used to know. And I can tell you miss him too. I'm sorry for both of you, but I guess the damage is done. So long, Victoria. Have a merry Christmas."

He waved to me and went out the door. I sat down at the counter and rested my head on my arms the way I used to at school. I wondered what Ivan would think when he found out I was going to have a baby. It would break his heart. He'd hate me more than ever. Dear God, if only I could tell him the truth. It would set his tortured mind at ease, and mine too. But I couldn't tell him! I just couldn't!

▦   ▦   ▦

I invited my whole family over for Christmas Eve. It was my first as a married woman and I wanted to show them I could manage on my own, with Petrusia's help of course. At dusk, with the cooking all done, Petrusia and I got the dining room ready. First we decorated the Christmas tree. Then we spread fresh hay on the table and covered it with a white embroidered tablecloth. Finally we set out the china and silver. When everything looked perfect, I went to get dressed while Petrusia cleaned up the pots and pans.

When the family arrived, everybody exchanged cheery greetings and sat down at the table. I lighted the wax candles on the tree and Grandfather said a prayer. He picked up the traditional Christmas wafer and broke it with his children and grandchildren.

"I wish you all merry Christmas and a happy new year," he said, looking into our faces one by one. "We have no knowledge of our destiny. We don't know what 1939 will bring. I hope it brings good health and good luck to all of us."

Then, as a symbol of good health, we shared some garlic and bread.

Dinner was noisy and cheerful. The meal consisted of borscht, pierogi, cabbage rolls, pickled herring, stuffed and baked fish, and a fruit compote. There was wine for the adults and tea with raspberry syrup for the children. After dinner Grandfather moved to the crackling fireplace and started a Christmas carol, his strong healthy bass ringing out loud and clear. Soon the others joined him and everybody began exchanging presents. By the time the last one was opened, it was time for midnight mass.

Jingling horse-drawn sleighs joined in the music as the ringing bells of the church drew young and old from all over town and from neighboring villages. Inside the church the music came from the organ in the choir loft, and from singing that came from the heart and the soul. It was as if all this magnificent worship was being sent up into the mountains and the mountains were echoing back.

"Yes, we hear you," they were saying. "We know that Jesus was born, and we join you in rejoicing."

After mass the night was bright as day, very cold and very quiet. People exchanged good wishes in clouds of breath that hung in the crisp air. Some climbed into sleighs and were towed off by eager horses venting steam from their nostrils. Others walked home through the deep snow that crunched under their feet. It was a beautiful night I would treasure and long remember.

※　　※　　※

Sheila Landow came home for the holidays and stopped by to see me. She wanted to know why Edward hadn't come home as he said he would. I took a letter out of my pocket.

"This just came to us," I said and unfolded it.

Sheila sat down on the edge of the chair, her hands trembling, and waited for me to read it.

"Sorry I never made it home for Christmas," I read aloud. "All leaves were unexpectedly canceled. Hope you weren't waiting for me. Tell Sheila I love her and miss her terribly, and will write her at school. Merry Christmas to all. Love, Eddie."

"May I see it?" Sheila asked.

I handed her the letter and watched as she ran her hands over the paper. It was as if she was drawing love from it.

"I'll never see him again," she said. "I know, something tells me."

"Sheila, don't say that," I said. "Of course you'll see him again. His letter says he's stationed in Przemysl, not far from where you go to school. You can see him there."

Sheila suddenly brightened. "Why didn't I think of that?"

I took her in my arms and embraced her.

"You're too much in love, that's why," I said. "Go, dear friend. Spend this precious time with the man you love. I'll see you in the summer."

※　※　※

Petrusia and I spent most of the last day of 1938 making donuts for the New Year's Eve charity ball. We arranged them on trays in stacks and sprinkled them with powdered sugar. Then we carried them to the hall and hurried home to dress. On the way back, I slipped on the ice and fell. Petrusia helped me to my feet and brushed off the snow. I thanked her without mentioning the sharp pain in my back.

We stayed at the ball until four in the morning. I had started to feel ill and persuaded my intoxicated husband to take me home. It was snowing hard so it took us nearly twice as long to get there. On the way, I became chilled and started to shake. Once in the house, Jan collapsed on the bed and fell asleep. I let him lie. My back was hurting more than ever and a pain had started in my belly. My only thought was to crawl under the covers and get warm.

When the pain grew more severe, I tried to rouse Jan but he didn't respond. I crawled out of bed and hobbled to Petrusia's room. Petrusia was on her feet instantly. She tucked me back into bed and shook Jan vigorously.

"You have to get the doctor," she said. "Missus is going to have a baby."

"You're crazy," Jan mumbled. "It's not time."

"I'm not crazy," Petrusia said. "Listen to her moaning."

Half drunk and half asleep, Jan put on his clothes and stumbled to the door.

"Nobody's going to come in weather like this," he said. "The storm is blowing fiercely and the snow is accumulating in drifts."

But by now my moans had turned into agonized cries for help.

"Get somebody!" Petrusia said urgently. "Or she's going to die!"

Jan staggered out into the strong wind and Petrusia ran back to the bedroom. I cried shrilly, arched my back rigidly and then suddenly I relaxed.

"Something big came out of me," I said.

Petrusia lifted the covers and looked. Her face turned white.

"My God, it's a baby!" she said.

I lay still, exhausted and frightened. Petrusia hurried to the window and scratched at the frosted pane.

"What am I going to do?" she wailed as she scurried back and forth between the bed and the window. "What am I going to do?"

Finally she said she could see figures trudging up to the house.

"The baby's already born!" I heard Petrusia exclaim as she opened the door.

Mr. and Mrs. Friedes hurried into the bedroom and quickly sized up the situation.

"Bring some gauze and scissors," Mrs. Friedes said.

When Petrusia brought them, Mrs. Friedes used the gauze to tie the cord that was attached to the baby. Then she cut the cord, wrapped the baby in a blanket, and put it into a basket.

"It's a boy," Mrs. Friedes said and showed him to me.

I smiled weakly and closed my eyes.

"He's very small and very weak," Mrs. Friedes whispered to her husband. "He doesn't have any hair or fingernails."

Mr. Friedes came closer and looked at the baby.

"He's premature," he said. "How can he survive? He's too small."

"He looks like a frog," Jan said indifferently.

I opened my eyes and saw Jan take a bottle of liquor out of the cabinet and fill some glasses. Despite the early hour, he insisted everybody join him in a toast. The Friedes obliged and then left. Jan continued drinking until he fell against the Christmas tree and toppled with it to the floor. I remembered that Petrusia threw a blanket over him and let him sleep where he lay, and then I fell asleep.

In the morning I awoke to a wind that was still howling. I asked for my son and Petrusia brought in the baby.

"He looks so tiny, like a little doll," I said, holding him close. "He can't be more than two pounds."

"If that," Petrusia said. "You'll need a bottle to feed him."

"No I won't. I'll nurse him."

But the baby was too weak to suckle, and my breasts were not yet ready with milk. I looked up, distraught.

"How am I going to feed him?" I asked.

"The milk will come," Petrusia said. "Until it does we can give him some herbal tea with sugar."

She went away to make it.

Jan came into the bedroom bleary-eyed and unshaven.

"He's ugly and small," he said staring down at the baby.

"He's beautiful!" I said. "But I'm having trouble feeding him."

"That's your problem," he said. "He's your baby."

"But you're his father!" I said angrily.

"Perhaps I am, but I've got other things to worry about."

He went out without another word.

"What a cold man he is," I said through my tears. "He has no heart, not even for his own son."

Petrusia came in with a warm cup of tea. She spooned a few drops into the baby's mouth. He swallowed them and I beamed.

"He'll grow, I know he will!" I said fondly. "I promise you."

But when Dr. Shline came to see me he shook his head.

"It'll be a miracle if the baby survives," he said. "You should be prepared for whatever happens."

"He'll survive," I said. "I'll do anything and everything to keep him alive. You see, he's mine and I love him. He's the only thing that I have to love, that's why he'll live—for me."

A week later my parents came to see the baby. I could tell that they too were not impressed, but this was their first grandson so they greeted us warmly.

"The baby won't live," Mother said to Father when she thought I wasn't listening. "Maybe it's for the best."

"For whom?" Father snapped angrily. "For Victoria? Or for you, because you don't like the idea of becoming a grandmother?"

Chapter Thirteen

*A*fter the holidays Sheila went back to school. She wrote me that she and Edward had arranged to meet in Przemysl in February, and that she would write again and tell me all about it. When her second letter came, I sat down to read it with great joy and anticipation.

I took the morning train and registered at the hotel, my heart pounding fiercely. I waited until late afternoon but Edward never showed up. A bad feeling suddenly came over me and I decided to go to the barracks where he was stationed. At the gate a young officer told me that Edward's company had just been sent to the German border. My heart sank.

I walked back to the hotel, my eyes glassy and filled with tears. I went to bed without supper and cried myself to sleep. The next morning, feeling empty and alone, I took the early train back to school. Now I'm sure I'll never see him again.

"But you will, Sheila," I found myself saying out loud. "I know you will!"

❖   ❖   ❖

It was May and spring was in full bloom again. Lilacs opened their tiny white and purplish flowers, blossoming into big bouquets on bushes throughout town, and sending their fragrance through the open windows and into the houses. I was sitting by the window, playing with my son Mitchel, enjoying the quiet of the advancing twilight.

"Petrusia, look!" I called. "He's smiling at me."

Petrusia came and bent over the crib.

"It's time for him to smile," she said. "He's growing nice and strong. You're going to have a beautiful son, Mrs. Hertig. You're very lucky."

"Thanks to your help," I said.

"I've never had a child of my own," Petrusia said. "Now I have a chance to raise this one. May I put him to bed for you?"

I let Petrusia take the baby away and walked out onto the porch. Darkness was slowly covering the earth but I didn't put on the light. I could hear grasshoppers singing on the lawn. The white roses on either side of the porch were in full flower. I inhaled the aromatic balsam-like air and watched the darkening sky slowly reveal a million twinkling stars.

"What a beautiful evening," I whispered and stretched my arms up. "An evening for lovers."

I brought my hands down to my lips and thought how much I would have liked to be loved at that moment! If only Ivan could have come and wrapped his arms around me and held me close to his heart! I would have probably fainted, or disappeared, or just submerged myself into him and stayed there forever.

The woman in me was awakening, starting to long for a man's love. I wrapped my arms around myself and held on tightly. That was how I wanted to be surrounded by him. How sweet that would have been. Ivan, why couldn't you step out of the darkness and love me?

I heard footsteps behind me and looked around. Jan had come out onto the porch.

"Beautiful evening, isn't it?" he said. He walked up and took my hand. "So very romantic."

I slipped my hand out of his and switched on the light.

"Why did you do that?" he asked. "You spoiled the mood."

"What mood? I was only looking to see if it was going to rain. But it isn't so I think I'll go to Zatwarnica in the morning."

"Really? Why?"

"To see my parents and to show off my baby. Now if you'll excuse me, I don't feel well. I'm going to my room."

▨   ▨   ▨

By noon the next day I arrived at my parents' house. Instead of having lunch as Mother asked, I put the baby in a carriage and went for a stroll. It was as if something was drawing me. I walked toward the apartments by the plant and chanced to see Zbyshek.

"Nice-looking baby," he said when he peered into the carriage. "But to me babies are babies."

I laughed. "Still living the dangerous life?"

"With the same married woman."

"Poor Zbyshek. If her husband finds out he'll kill you."

"I think he knows but pretends he doesn't," Zbyshek said. "If that's the way he wants it, it's fine with me. How long are you staying in town?"

"I'm going back home this afternoon," I said. "Late afternoon."

Zbyshek waved goodbye and headed for the village. I crossed the small bridge to my grandfather's estate and walked into the meadow. The trees were covered with tiny apples and pears. I sat down on the grass and looked up at the sky. The sun was high and warm on my face. How beautiful it was when I used to come here and play. That was a long time ago. I was a little girl then. Now I'm a woman and a mother.

The smile disappeared from my face and tears filled my eyes as my thoughts drifted to Ivan.

"Where are you, my love? What are you doing now? Please answer me."

But no answer came, only the blowing of the gentle breeze and the sound of the grasshoppers. I lay there for a long time, daydreaming, when something caused me to sit up. I saw a figure walking toward me. As the figure drew near I saw to my astonishment that it was Ivan. Ivan!

I stood up and started to wave but drew my hand down to my heart. I could feel it pounding under my blouse. As Ivan came closer I could see he was wearing short pants and a white short-sleeve shirt. His muscular legs and arms were tanned. His blues eyes shone and there were small beads of perspiration on his forehead as if he had been running. He came up to me, took my hand and kissed it warmly.

"I'm sorry for what happened between us," I said.

"For God's love, why?" Ivan said. "You knew I loved you, and I know you cared for me. When you were getting married, I cursed you for it. But what if it wasn't your fault, I asked myself. What if you were forced into that marriage by unusual or mysterious circumstances? What if you're an innocent victim and I'm judging you so harshly? Then I'm at fault."

I lifted my eyes to him and they filled with tears.

"I was told to marry Jan Hertig," I said. "I couldn't do anything about it."

"Every night your face appeared before me," he said. "Your smiling dark eyes, your lips fresh and moist like cherries picked from a tree—lips I was afraid to touch, afraid to take away the beauty of your innocence with a single kiss. I was saving all those precious kisses for when you grew to be a woman and then we would marry. Oh God, what joy that would have been. What glory would have enchanted my heart."

"It was my parents' decision, not mine," I said. "I obeyed them, and there's nothing more to say."

Heart aching, I started to push the carriage away but Ivan stopped it with his hand.

"I'd like to see your baby," he said.

I gave him a teary look and drew back the sunshade.

"This is my son," I said, "the only thing in this world that I love. I'm glad to have him."

Ivan looked down at the baby and smiled.

"You're very lucky," he said. "I have no one. I can't love anyone else. I tried, but I love only you. And I apologize for cursing you at your wedding. My heart was bleeding and the pain was great. I didn't know what I was saying."

I nodded my head in bitter acceptance.

"If you're ever in trouble or pain," he went on, "come to me. My heart is open to you and will stay open for the rest of my life. Come any time. I'll take you and lock you in my heart forever. I ask only one thing of you. Do you love Jan Hertig?"

"No," I answered. "I do not."

"Do you love me?"

"Ivan, please don't ask me that! I can't answer. I'm married."

Like a string of pearls suddenly broken, tears rolled down my cheeks.

Ivan took my hand and kissed it passionately.

"Goodbye, my love," he said. "I know you love me. Your tears have answered my question and filled my heart with joy." He plucked a small white daisy out of the grass and handed it to me. "This will be our flower, yours and mine. Every time you see one it will remind you of me, and me of you."

I held the little flower close as I watched him turn and walk away. He never looked back.

"Yes, this will be our flower," I said softly. "And I'll love you forever as long as I live. Thank you for telling me that you harbor no bitterness for me, only love. How great is your heart! How sweet and honest is your love!"

Chapter Fourteen

*T*he summer of 1939 was pleasant. The days were hot but the nights were cooled by fresh breezes. Jan was preparing to leave town for a buying trip but before going he tried on his uniform.

"Where'd you get that?" I asked as he posed in front of the mirror. He looked remarkably distinguished.

"Reservists with rank keep their uniforms at home," Jan said. "I expect I'll be needing it soon. The situation is growing more serious by the hour. Czechoslovakia has already been seized by the Germans and they will probably try to take us on next. But we'll be ready for them."

Jan put his uniform away and left. I was always glad to see him go. It gave me a temporary sense of freedom.

Petrusia and I were cleaning house when Edward surprised us by walking in. He looked especially handsome in his uniform.

"Eddie! How wonderful to see you!" I said and gave him a sisterly hug and kiss. "Why didn't you tell us you were coming?"

"I got my leave at the last minute," he said.

"Too bad. You just missed Jan."

"I didn't come to see my brother," he said with a wink.

I laughed. "Petrusia, go fetch Sheila."

Petrusia gave Edward a brief hug and dashed out of the house.

"Is it all right to bring Sheila here?" Edward asked.

"Of course it is," I said. "Make yourself at home. Petrusia and I have lots of things to keep us busy elsewhere in the house."

I retreated discreetly into the kitchen to make tea. When I heard the door open a few minutes later, I heard Sheila's cry and imagined the two lovers falling into each other's arms. How lovely this night will be for them. It may be the brightest night in their lives. I felt a pang of envy until I remembered that I too had a great and undying love. At least Sheila's was being somewhat fulfilled, and I was glad that I had been able to play a small part in bringing them together.

Petrusia came into the kitchen and giggled into her apron.

"I don't think they'll be wanting tea," she said blushing. "Is it all right if they stay in Eddie's room?"

"Jan won't be home to raise the roof for at least a few days," I said. "By then they'll be gone."

After an all-too-short period of bliss, Sheila and I took Edward to the station. We heard the whistle from a distance and Sheila jumped as if she had been pierced by a knife. I hung back as the two lovers walked out onto the platform. Edward gave Sheila a last kiss and climbed on board the hissing train. He waved and the door closed behind him. The whistle blew and the big wheels squealed as the train started to roll. Sheila and I watched the last car disappear behind the mountain.

"I'll never see him again," Sheila said through tears.

"That's what you thought before," I said. "But he came back, didn't he?"

"He did," Sheila said. "I was wrong, and apologize for not trusting in God. I hope my prayers will be answered again soon."

"I'm sure they will," I reassured her. "A love like yours is so special it deserves to live."

On the first day of September the cool breezes of fall were already making themselves felt. I announced to Petrusia that my parents were coming to visit. I would do the marketing if Petrusia prepared my father's favorite dinner. Petrusia gladly agreed, if only to have the kitchen to herself.

I put the baby in the carriage and walked past the Friedes house. Mrs. Friedes looked up from cutting dahlias and smiled happily at me and the baby.

"What a perfect day for a stroll with the little one," she said. "I remember how tiny he was when he was born. Who can say there are no miracles? I see one right before my eyes."

"I'll always be grateful for your help on that cold winter night," I said.

I wished Mrs. Friedes a pleasant day and continued on to the square. The church bells were ringing for the last morning mass. Wagons were rumbling by filled with produce that the farmers were hawking with rhythmic chants. Kitchen maids scurried to fill their little baskets with fresh vegetables, meat, milk and eggs. The town was awakening and people were going about their business.

Suddenly the siren on the town hall blew two short blasts and one very long one. People came out of their shops and houses and looked around. Jan saw me in the square and came over. We were joined by Mr. Zawacki, the owner of the liquor store.

"What happened?" I asked. "What's going on?"

"I don't know," Jan said.

"It's either the Russians or the Germans," Zawacki said. "They are both sitting on our borders like vultures."

A man came out of the town hall holding a sheet of paper in one hand and a megaphone in the other. He proceeded to the middle of the square and was soon surrounded. He put the megaphone close to his mouth and read from the paper.

"This morning at dawn," he said loudly, "German troops crossed the frontier and invaded Poland. All men in military service must report to their stations at once. We are at war. God help us."

"God help the Jews," Zawacki muttered.

"Long live Poland!" the man shouted through the megaphone.

The crowd replied, "Long live Poland!"

But their voices quickly died and there was silence, a great silence. A woman dropped to her knees and started to pray. Others joined her. Tears ran down women's cheeks and men's faces grew pale, their lips whispering prayers. The crowd started to disperse, slowly at first and then faster, everybody running in different directions. I found myself nearly alone in the square, frozen with fear. Even Jan had disappeared.

"We should be prepared," Zawacki said. "We should store some food away, and hide our possessions and valuables. I will start tonight."

Zawacki hurried off. I turned the carriage around and headed for home. I saw Mr. and Mrs. Friedes in tears in the front yard, holding each other.

"What's going to happen now?" I asked anxiously.

"Only God knows, my young friend," Mrs. Friedes said. "Only God knows."

The church bells started ringing loudly as they did on Christmas or Easter. Wagons flew by, pulled by galloping horses. I arrived home to find Jan putting on his uniform.

"The carriages will be picking us up at the courthouse," was all he said.

"What about us?" I asked. "Who'll take care of me and the baby?"

"You'll be all right. You can take care of the house and the business while I go and kill a few Germans." He kissed me and the baby. "I'll be back before you know it."

I followed Jan out of the house, my eyes wide open, ready to ask a million questions, but he left without another word and ran to the courthouse. Some of the carriages were already there and Jan climbed aboard with the other men. They were laughing and waving to the people who were watching.

Petrusia came over and put her arm around me.

"They act like they're going on a picnic, not to war," I said. "And he's not worried about me or the baby. My God, Petrusia, what if the Germans come here? What will they do to us?"

"Nothing will happen to you and the baby as long as I'm with you," Petrusia said. "I won't allow it."

I hugged Petrusia and watched the loaded carriages start to move off. People on the street were singing the national anthem and waving Polish flags.

"He really doesn't care," I muttered under my breath. "He just up and left. Well good! He can just go to hell!"

A carriage bearing my parents came from the other direction at great speed. I brightened as Father pulled up the horses and jumped down.

"Pack your things," he said without bothering to greet me. "You and the baby are coming with us."

"We're not going anywhere," I said. "My husband told me to take care of the business and I plan to do just that."

"Victoria, darling, be reasonable," Mother said. "If the soldiers come and you're alone they'll hurt you or even kill you."

"God knows what could happen to you and the baby," Father said. "You must come home with us."

"I'm a married woman," I said with some irony. "You saw to that. I'm going to stay here the way a married woman should, and take care of myself and Mitchel."

Dr. Shline and Mr. Friedes came hurrying by.

"Where are you going so fast?" I asked.

"To the synagogue," Mr. Friedes said. "We're in God's hands now. Only prayer can save us."

"We may be in Hitler's hands soon," Dr. Shline said. "So we have to think of how we're going to protect ourselves. We've all heard what they're doing to Jews."

"Maybe it's not true," I said.

Dr. Shline touched my cheek. "Pray to God it's not, my child." He looked around wistfully. "I was born in this town, as was my father and his father. And now this."

"I heard on the radio that the Russians are marching toward the Polish frontier," Mr. Friedes said to my father. "Do you think they will help us?"

Father shook his head sadly. "Would you rather see Russians in Poland, or Germans?"

"I'd rather see the devil," Dr. Shline said.

"We may get to see them all," Father said.

Dr. Shline and Mr. Friedes continued on their way, talking and gesturing excitedly as they walked.

Father turned to Petrusia and held her hand.

"Watch over our daughter and her baby," he said. "If you think she should come home to us, send them—if you have to, by force—but send them."

"I'll watch over them," Petrusia said as she held me close. "I promise."

Chapter Fifteen

S ince I was all alone, Mr. and Mrs. Friedes came to keep me company. Petrusia served tea and cookies and we listened to the late news on the radio.

"Warsaw is being bombed!" an announcer shouted through the heavy static. *"The first bombs have fallen on Warsaw!"*

"Dear God," Mrs. Friedes said, "what's going to happen to us now? Where are we going to hide? They'll kill us all!"

Mr. Friedes patted his wife's hand and turned to me.

"Why didn't you leave with your parents?" he asked. "This is war, child, don't you understand? A horrible war has stretched its wings over us. Go tomorrow while there's still time."

For the first time I realized something big and very frightening was happening. Something unknown to me. That night I went to church. The church was packed and a crowd of people stood outside. After a special mass for the survival of Poland, everyone joined in a novena for dying soldiers. It was close to midnight when devotions ended.

I couldn't cry like many of the others in the church. I was numb and lonely and beginning to feel possessed by great fear. I also felt abandoned by my parents. If they really wanted me to go home with them, why didn't they make me go? Why didn't they try harder to convince a daughter they know is stubborn?

But for some reason I no longer felt abandoned by Jan. In fact I was glad he had gone to war. Maybe he would be lost and then my life would change.

I didn't sleep well that night. I kept listening for noises and watching the window, expecting Germans to come at any moment and drag me from my bed. I pictured them as devils from hell and imagined the torture they would inflict on me. Just before dawn I left my room and crawled into Petrusia's bed. In the morning I apologized for doing so.

"I'm glad you came into my bed," Petrusia said. "I was scared too."

We both laughed. In my heart I knew Petrusia was lying, but I left it at that.

There was a hard knock on the door and Petrusia opened it. Four men were standing there. One of them addressed me in Ukrainian.

"Over the years I've done work in your husband's shop," he said. "We know Mr. Hertig's gone to war and will never come back, so we decided you should give us all his clothes."

Petrusia became angry and picked up a pot.

"Get out of here!" she shouted. "You came to rob Mrs. Hertig because you know she's alone, but I won't permit it! Get out!"

"Stop!" I said. "I'll give them what they want, but I'll report them to the police."

"There are no police," the man laughed. "They ran away last night. It's every man for himself. If you give us what we want we'll watch over you so nobody else will rob you."

I led the men into the bedroom, opened the closet and took out everything that was Jan's. I dumped it all onto the bed—shirts, shoes, suits. One of the men picked up a black suit.

"Your husband's wedding suit?" he asked.

I nodded.

"We'll leave it," he said and put it back in the closet. "That way you'll have something to remember him by."

The men pulled up the bedspread, tied it around the pile of clothes and carried everything out. I closed the door behind them and locked it with trembling hands. I felt pale as a ghost.

"They could have killed me!" I said to Petrusia. "And there's no one here to protect us. My father was right. Why didn't I listen?"

"You must go home today," Petrusia said. "I'll help you get ready."

"No," I said, getting control of myself. "Maybe nothing more will happen. I still have to take care of the shop. I can bring home all the merchandise and store it in the basement. That way if we need food we'll be able to trade it for tobacco and cigarettes."

When I got to the shop the door was wide open. The shop was empty. Everything had been taken. Mr. Zawacki came in and looked around.

"Just like mine," he said. "Everything gone."

"They even came into my house and took my husband's clothes!"

"What? Who?"

"Some men who used to work for him."

"The scoundrels!" Zawacki snarled. "I'll go and speak to them!"

He left and I picked up a broken piece of glass from the counter. I stared it for a moment and then angrily threw it against the wall. It shattered into small pieces.

"I'm never coming back here, ever!" I said in frustration. "Jan can come and watch his cursed shop by himself. I don't ever want to see it again!"

⊠　　⊠　　⊠

A week passed and nothing unusual happened. No police, no soldiers, no Germans, no Russians. People walked around bewildered. The radio said Poland was winning. Warsaw was holding fast and now was not the time to give up hope. God would help, and of course so would England and France. Everybody would help and eventually Poland would win. Hope filled people's hearts and their spirits started to grow. They formed a militia and order was restored.

I was talking to Mr. Friedes when a young boy on a horse came galloping past.

"Horsemen in the forest!" he shouted. "They're watching our town and waiting!"

"Quickly!" Mr. Friedes said and gave me a push. "Hide yourself and the baby in the basement!"

I ran back to my house and had barely closed the door when a horde of horsemen came galloping into town, yelling and screaming. They were at least two hundred in number, dressed in white shirts with red or blue pants and high boots. I watched them charge up and down the streets like invaders from hell, trampling people under their horses' hooves and smashing windows and doors. Then, as quickly as they came, they left.

I ventured outside. Lutowiska looked like a battlefield. There was glass all over from the pillaged shops. Men, women and children were lying in the street moaning and sobbing. Some had broken arms and legs, others had bleeding heads and faces. It was our first taste of war, and the taste was bitter.

Sheila and her father brought a coach to my house.

"You're too young for war," Sheila said to me. "You must go home to your family. There'll be no one here to look after you."

I started to say something.

"Please don't argue," Sheila said. "There isn't much time."

"My man will take you home to Zatwarnica," Mr. Landow said. "We'll help you get your things."

Petrusia agreed and together we quickly loaded my things and the baby into the coach. Petrusia gave us a last hug and kiss.

"God bless," she said.

"God bless," I replied.

Sheila grasped my hand. "Something tells me we may never meet again."

"Sheila!" I admonished her. "You're always saying that. But you'll see, we'll be together again soon. All of us!"

The coach took off at full speed and in two hours we reached the bridge over the River San. We started across but were stopped by soldiers on the other side.

"Germans!" the coachman said and drew up the horses.

One of the soldiers came over and said something in German that I couldn't understand. I was bewildered, my heart was pounding wildly.

"Do you know what he said?" I asked the coachman.

"We're not allowed to cross," the coachman said. "This is the German occupied zone."

"Tell him my father lives in Zatwarnica. Tell him my baby and I want to go home."

The coachman said something in German but the soldier just shook his head.

"We have to go back," the coachman said.

"Please let me cross," I pleaded, and added in German, *"Bitte!"*

But the soldier was unmoved and pointed in the direction from which we had come. The coachman turned the horses around and headed back to Lutowiska. I looked over my shoulder at the other side of the river and tears ran down my cheeks.

It was dark by the time we got home.

"All saints!" Petrusia said and took the baby from me.

I thanked the coachman and told him to thank Mr. Landow for me. Then I followed Petrusia into the house and told her what happened.

"There are no Germans here," Petrusia said, "so maybe you're safer here after all."

I slept well knowing the baby and I were back under the watchful eyes of Petrusia. In some ways I felt more secure than with my own parents. The next morning everything looked much better. Calm had returned to our town and even Mrs. Friedes was out in her flower garden.

"Good morning!" I called out.

As Mrs. Friedes started to answer, we heard people singing. We looked to see where the sound was coming from. Down the street, a large group of people were approaching. They were marching in good order and singing with energy and conviction. The man in front was carrying a red banner.

"Where are you going?" I asked one of them as they marched past.

"To greet the Russian army," the man said proudly. "They're coming today!"

Petrusia came out of the house, a puzzled look on her face.

"Why are they singing the Russian national anthem?" she asked. "They're mostly Jews."

"Because the Russians are coming!" I said with alarm.

※　　※　　※

At three o'clock in the afternoon, the ground started to shake like thunder, growing louder and louder. A huge tank rolled into town—first one, then two, then three, then more and more. After the tanks came trucks full of soldiers. They encircled the town and stopped. A few tanks parked in the middle of the square. A Russian officer climbed up onto one of them.

"Citizens and comrades," he said over a loudspeaker, "we are your friends. We're here to protect you. We want all of you to come to the square tonight and get to know us. We're here to help you."

When the officer finished, the townspeople left and hid in their houses. Later in the evening they came back to the square and started to mingle with the soldiers. The soldiers were very polite, hugging the men and women and kissing the children. Then the Russian officer turned on the loudspeaker again.

"I speak to you in the name of the U.S.S.R. and my comrades in arms," he said. "We are your allies and your friends, and we want to live with you in peace and harmony. But you have to understand that we are the Red Army, so you must cooperate. We need quarters for the brave soldiers who are defending you. We'll be sending men to look at your houses. We don't expect any resistance. We come as friends, let us stay friends. And now, some music to cheer you up."

Music burst out of the loudspeaker, very loud and very hectic.

I turned to Mrs. Friedes. "What a difference from our music."

"Yes," Mrs. Friedes whispered. "Now we will all sing and dance to their tune. How ironic."

That evening I heard a truck pull into the back yard and heavy boots walk toward the house. There was a banging on the door. Petrusia opened it and a Russian officer came in. Behind him were two women in uniform, and behind them three more officers. They passed by us and walked through the house.

"We'll take six rooms, Comrade Hertig," one of them said. "You, the baby and this woman can have the other."

"Three of us in one room?" I managed to ask even though I was shaking with fear.

"You can use the room you are sleeping in now, and you can use the kitchen," the officer said. "You're not allowed to go anywhere else."

He gave orders to the others and they tramped in and out of the house, bringing in all kinds of bags. It had started to rain and Petrusia kept staring at their dirty boots.

"I think I'm losing my mind," she whispered to me. "Here they're taking our house and country and all I'm worrying about is the mud they're tracking across the floor."

I drew her aside.

"Your room is the safest," I said. "It has only one door. We'll move in with you."

Petrusia quickly moved the baby while I transferred my clothes and the suitcases that were still packed.

"I'd like some tea," one of the Russian women said to me. "Can you make it for me?"

"Yes," I said.

Petrusia heard this and went to kindle the fire in the brick stove.

"Who is this woman?" the Russian asked.

"I'm her aunt," Petrusia said before I could open my mouth. "Her husband went to war. She's afraid to be alone."

"She doesn't have to be afraid anymore," the Russian said. "She'll be safe now that we're here."

Chapter Sixteen

I didn't sleep well with Russian soldiers in the house. I got up early and tried to use the bathroom but it was occupied. When I finally squeezed in I washed up quickly and retreated to my room.

Petrusia went to the kitchen to fix breakfast but it was being used by the soldiers. She went to the barn to milk the cows. To her horror she saw that one of the cows had been butchered and was being carefully cut up by soldiers. She ran back into the house.

"They butchered our cow!" she said to me. "How dare they!"

"Don't yell, woman!" one of the officers said. "Fighting men have to eat, and you have more cows in the barn. Take care of them. We need the milk."

I exchanged despairing glances with Petrusia. There was nothing else for us to do. It seemed that I had spent my entire life being obedient to somebody—first my parents, then my husband, and now the Russians. Was there no end to it?

On the third day of occupation I went for a walk through town. The Friedes had two Russians living with them, as did nearly everybody else. The Landows, however, had no soldiers in the house.

"My father is worried why they haven't touched us," Sheila said.

"Be glad," I said. "The Russians are very dirty. They have lice on their clothes. We keep our room locked and try not to touch anything that they touch."

"If you can't stay there," Sheila said, "pack up your baby and move in with us. My family and I will look after you. Remember that."

I thanked her and walked on feeling better that somebody in town actually cared for me. In the square I saw Russian soldiers drinking vodka, playing their accordions and singing and dancing the kozak, their beloved Russian dance. The townspeople were standing around watching and smiling but I knew that in their hearts they were cursing, praying that the Russians would leave as fast as they had come. Only it didn't look like they were getting ready to leave. It looked like they were making themselves comfortable and planning to stay for a long time.

When I got home one of the officers directed me into the room that had once been my bedroom. It was now an office.

"Comrade, I'm going to ask you some questions," he said. "I want you to tell me the truth."

I nodded.

"Where's your husband?"

"Fighting Germans."

The officer nodded with satisfaction. "Where's the rest of your family? Your mother and father?"

"In Zatwarnica, on the other side of the River San."

"Under German occupation?"

"I think so."

"You think so?" the officer snapped.

I jumped.

"Do you like Germans?" he asked.

"No!"

"Do you like Russians?"

"No! I mean yes."

"Are you a *kulak*?"

"I don't know what that is."

"Are you rich?"

"I have a house. I had a business, my husband's business, but I don't have one now. It was robbed. I used to have cows, horses and pigs but I don't have them either."

"Why not?"

"Your soldiers took them and ate them, that's why," I said cautiously displaying my anger.

The officer stared at me for a while.

"You can go," he said.

I went back to my room and closed the door. I sat down on the bed, unbuttoned my blouse and started to nurse the baby. Suddenly the door swung open. I thought it was Petrusia but when I lifted my head I saw the Russian officer standing in the doorway. I didn't make a move or a sound. I just looked at him.

He came in without a word and closed the door behind him. He came close to me, grabbed the baby from my arms and threw the baby on the bed. The baby started to cry. The officer made a move as if he was going to grab me and I pushed myself higher on the bed, away from him. My breast was out of my dress, still wet from the baby's sucking. He grabbed me with his big rough hands and squeezed me in his strong arms. He pressed his mouth close to my face trying for my lips.

"No, no!" I gasped and turned my head away.

He became violent and started tearing my clothes off. The baby rolled from the bed and fell on the floor, crying loudly. The Russian threw himself on me and shoved his face in my breast. He took it in his mouth and bit hard. I cried out in pain just as Petrusia opened the door.

"What are you doing to her?" Petrusia shouted and started to drag him off. "Leave her alone or I'll kill you!"

The Russian released his hold on me and stood up. His face had the look of a wild animal whose attack had been foiled.

"Bitch!" he snarled at Petrusia.

He hit her in the face with such power that she fell to the floor.

"I'll get you later," he said to me as he adjusted his uniform and went out.

I was shaking as I picked up my crying baby and tried to quiet him. I put the baby on the bed and helped Petrusia to her feet.

"The bastard," Petrusia said. "I'll report him to his superior. But you're bleeding. What did he do to you?"

I looked down at my breast and touched it.

"It hurts!" I said. "That Russian pig bit me. He would have raped me if you hadn't walked in."

"You should go see Dr. Shline," Petrusia said. "Who knows how that mad dog may have infected you."

"I want to go home!" I said suddenly. "I can't stay here one minute longer!"

"You can't go home. They won't let you across the bridge."

"Then I'll find another way."

"You'd have to go through the forest, and you don't know it well enough."

"Please, Petrusia, don't try to stop me," I said. "You heard what that awful man said about getting me later!"

Petrusia stroked my head.

"I couldn't stop you if I tried, could I?" she said sadly.

I shook my head with determination.

"First I will take you to see Dr. Shline," Petrusia said. "Then we will find a way to get you home."

Petrusia fed the baby and dressed him in a warm suit and cap, and wrapped him in a big shawl. I put on a sweater, some walking shoes and a coat, and the three of us went out. The officer who had attacked me stopped us.

"Where are you going?" he asked.

"Into town," Petrusia answered sharply. "To see the doctor."

Petrusia left us at the doctor's office and hurried off. Dr. Shline washed my breast with a sterile solution and put a bandage on it. By the time we came out, Petrusia was waiting for us with a boy of about fourteen.

"You can't use the road because the Russians require a pass," she said. "This boy can take you through the forest to the river. But what will you do then?"

"Wait until dark and sneak across the bridge," I said.

Petrusia hesitated, not knowing whether to believe me. But she could tell from the look of apprehension on my face that it would be futile to try to talk me out of it. Going forward into the unknown would be far less fearful to me than going back to the known. She embraced me and kissed the baby.

"God be with you," she said, "and be very careful."

I squeezed Petrusia's hand and held on to it as if I didn't want to let go. "Thank you for all you've done. God bless."

"God bless," Petrusia replied.

The words rang in my ears as I followed the boy through the forest. I would need God's help even though the boy seemed to know the area well. He stepped lightly between the branches and moved quickly as a cat.

I'm completely alone for the first time in my life, I thought as I tried to keep up. No parents, no husband, no Petrusia, just me. If I'm to live, I mustn't lose courage. No time for tears or fears. I have to think fast and be extremely careful or I'll die and my son with me.

After walking for two hours I called out to the boy.

"I'd like to sit for a while and nurse the baby," I said.

"Good," the boy answered. "You can do that because I can't go any farther."

A great fear seized me but I didn't say anything.

"From now on it'll be much easier for you," he said. "It's downhill all the way. Keep going straight until you come to a small stream, then follow it to the River San. But be careful. It's easy to get lost in these woods."

"God bless you for taking us this far," I said.

"God bless you on your journey," the boy said and disappeared into the forest.

I rested for a while and nursed the baby. Then I stood up and made the sign of the cross.

"I'm in your hands, God," I said and started to walk.

The forest was very quiet. I could hear the wind blowing through the tops of the tall pines. Once in a while I saw a rabbit race by or a squirrel dance swiftly across the branches. Then it started to rain and the forest grew dark.

I held the baby close to keep him warm. Perspiration covered my face from moving rapidly but I kept walking steadily according to the boy's instructions. Soon I heard the whisper of water and followed the sound to a small stream. It was very shallow, barely covering the stones, but the water was clear. I knelt and scooped some into my mouth. It was cold and tasted good.

The rain was falling harder. I followed the stream through heavy brush that covered both sides. Fallen trees and slippery rocks blocked the way. I scrambled over them and fell many times until suddenly the forest ended and I found myself at the edge of a meadow. I looked around but saw no one. I continued walking close to the stream where the brush shielded me from unwanted eyes. There were farmers in the fields hoeing potatoes but nobody bothered to look up. I came across some straw-roofed houses that looked empty and hurried past them. My Uncle Leon and his family lived somewhere near here but I wasn't sure where. Suddenly there was the river.

I stopped short when I heard voices below the embankment. Footsteps crunched on dead leaves and branches. I crouched in the brush, afraid to breathe. I heard voices and recognized the language as Russian. Through the branches I could see two sentries with their dogs, and beyond them the bridge with more sentries on it.

My God, I thought, I'll never make it to the bridge. What am I going to do?

As I waited for dark my eyes turned slowly to the river. I watched it helplessly. The river was full and the water was brown. It was running wildly, making frightening noises as it hit against its banks.

I couldn't go back, I decided. I would get lost and die. And if I stayed there, the Russians and their dogs would find me and tear me apart. If I chose the river I would never make it. But God help me, there was no other way. I had to choose the river!

The sentries walked past and Mitchel started to cry. I put my breast into the baby's mouth to keep him quiet. I pressed him so close I almost choked him. The sentries continued on without stopping. It was dark enough and time to run. I unwrapped the shawl from around Mitchel and tied two ends together to make a bag. The other two ends I tied around my neck. I took off my coat and shoes and stood up. I could hear the dogs barking. The sentries were coming back. I quickly slid down the steep embankment. I could hear water splashing. It was just in front of me. I crossed myself.

"Dear Jesus, I'm in your hands."

I took a few steps and was suddenly in deep water. I started to swim, holding my head high to keep the baby above water. I pulled with all my strength, praying with every stroke.

"Holy Mother of God, if I drown, take me with you to Heaven! Holy Mother of God, give me strength. I'm tired and weak. Please help me!"

It was totally dark. I couldn't see how far I had gone. I could feel the baby on my neck moving and crying. His voice was weak but he was alive. Maybe I would make it and maybe he wouldn't drown.

The current was strong and started to pull me down with it. I could feel that I was not swimming in the right direction. But I put up a good fight and called on the last of my strength. Finally the swimming became easier.

"A little more, a little more, Holy Mother of God. Stay with me for a little longer."

My hand hit something hard—a branch sticking out of the water. A few more strokes and I was able to grasp it. I realized I was close to the bank. I let the river float me in until I could feel the ground. Then I crawled out of the water and lay on the slimy and muddy ground. I had lost my strength and couldn't move but I was breathing and I was safe—alive and safe. Something moved on my neck and a little squeak came out, weak as a kitten. I lifted myself up and untied the shawl. My baby was shaking but he was alive.

"Thank you God, my Father," I said. "Thank you Holy Mother of God. Thank you for saving my life and the life of my son."

I grasped my son to my breast, warming him with my body, and stood up. I started to walk towards a small light that I recognized as coming from the lumberyard. As I came close I saw two sentries near the river. I hid behind a stack of lumber and the baby started to cry. The sentries stopped and said something to each other in German. But they walked on and went into the building.

I started to run, hiding behind the logs, jumping from one to the other, trying to stay in the shadows. My bare feet were being cut on the old wood. I ran between the employees' apartments and reached the garden. From there I could see my parents' house. Not clearly, only a shadow. The night was very dark. It was now raining very hard. I looked around and saw no one. I crept up to the house and tapped on the window. I waited. No one came. I tapped again, this time louder. My father came to the window and drew back the curtain.

"My sweet Jesus!" he said when he looked out. "Victoria!"

Chapter Seventeen

I had gotten a bad chill from swimming across the river. Father was afraid I had pneumonia. And now that Lutowiska was in the Russian zone, the nearest doctor was a day's travel away in Baligrod. It was too far for me to go so Father brought a woman from the village who was supposed to know something about healing.

The woman set out two dozen small glasses. She stripped me naked and had me lie on my stomach. She smeared the inside of one of the glasses with rubbing alcohol and dropped in a lighted match. *Puff!* The flame engulfed the interior of the glass. With the flame still burning she applied the glass to my back. I flinched from the pain. The flame died out and my skin was sucked up into the glass by the vacuum.

The woman repeated this until all the glasses were sticking to my back. Then she started to take them off with great skill. I started to breathe easier. On every spot where the glasses had been there was a big blister. In a few days I recuperated from the suspected pneumonia but the healing of the blisters took two months.

In October, I was having dinner with my parents when news came that the war with Germany was over. Poland had been conquered in less than four weeks.

"Poland is no more," Jan Kopp said sadly. "The Russian devil made a pact with the German devil, and divided our homeland between them."

"That's not all they've taken," I said. "I saw our new Ukrainian mayor driving around in one of grandfather's coaches."

"Don't blame Mayor Kochut," Father said. "The Germans gave it to him when they appointed him. They also took away my job."

"What do you mean?" Mother asked.

"They gave it to a Ukrainian from another village. I'm now a common laborer in the yard."

"My God!" Mother said. "Your pay was barely enough as it was."

"I know," Father said. "There's not much to be grateful for these days. At least our boys will be coming home soon."

"And they can start taking care of their families," Mother said pointedly with a glance at me.

A week later, to my stunned surprise, Jan showed up in Zatwarnica just as my father had predicted.

"Where did you come from?" I said, trying to hide my disappointment. "I thought for sure you'd been lost in the war."

"The Germans can't kill me," Jan said. "I was on my way home to Lutowiska when a neighbor told me you and Petrusia were no longer in the house and Russians were living in it. I guessed you had to be here so I came through the forest and stole across the river." He laughed. "Right under the sentries' noses, too. They're not so clever, these Russians and Germans."

Jan took a job in the sawmill and moved us into one of the small apartments provided for workers. It was really a loft with no running water. I had to go down to the river with buckets and carry them up the hill and then up two flights of stairs. Jan never helped. He said it was woman's work.

I was miserable. Mitchel had become sick with the whooping cough, and we had no medicine to give him. Food was also scarce but at least we had ration stamps. The Jews had none. The Germans must have believed that Jews didn't have to eat like everybody else. What little money Jan earned he spent on drink and cards. When I begged him to stop my pleas only served to enrage him. He struck me each time I complained so I tried not to complain at all.

I considered going to my parents for help but I was too ashamed. I didn't want to upset my father who wasn't feeling well, and I was afraid my mother would take Jan's side. My suspicions were confirmed when one day I mentioned his abusive ways.

"If you keep your mouth shut, he won't beat you," Mother said.

That was my first and last complaint to my mother.

After every beating Jan's apology was always to come to bed and mount me whether I liked it or not. He believed this was his right and he treated me like property. I soon discovered I was pregnant and was horrified at first. Mitchel was only nine months old and I was still only seventeen. Yet waiting for the baby which was alive in me kept me calm and somehow blissful. I believed every pregnant woman probably shared those same feelings.

Chapter Eighteen

That winter was very harsh. Cold seeped into the apartment from around the loose windows. The brick stove in the kitchen provided heat during the day when I was able to collect kindling but at night the fire died out and the water froze in the buckets. To stay warm, all three of us slept in one bed.

I bought potatoes from the Ukrainian farmers and stored them in a corner of the kitchen. I also bought cabbage which I shredded into a small barrel to ferment into sauerkraut. And my mother let us have a cow so there would be milk for the baby. The baby's health was slowly improving but he still had a cough.

One day I was grating potatoes for pancakes when I scraped my finger. I wrapped a piece of cloth around it and forgot about it. But a few days later my whole hand was red and swollen. The finger had turned blue from infection and I was beginning to feel feverish. I tried all the old-fashioned remedies like soaking my hand but nothing seemed to help. The infection only got worse. I started to get frightened. I knew that if I didn't take care of this problem I would die and my unborn baby would die with me. Then there was Mitchel, so little and so sick. Who would take care of him?

I asked my parents for advice and Father said there was no choice. Jan would have to take me to the doctor in Baligrod.

"I would take you myself," he said, "but I'm not feeling well, and it's a husband's duty."

"My husband knows his rights," I said. "But I don't think he knows his duties."

"Then I will enlighten him," Father said.

Jan was not excited at the prospect of hiking through the snow-covered mountains with a pregnant woman, but he agreed to go. It may have been because I asked the young woman neighbor to come with us. Her name was Tania and she had taken a fancy to Jan, which didn't bother me at all.

Snow in the mountains was waist deep. Villagers trudged from house to house like awakened bears. But this was their life. In the winter, the women spun and weaved linen while the men cleaned and fixed their farm equipment. In the evening the young people gathered in one house and talked politics or sang. Old people gathered in another house and drank homemade whiskey.

It took us about three hours to reach the top of the first mountain. There were at least seven more to go and I could already feel pain in my groin. We pushed on, stopping along the way to share whiskey with farmers who then shared their food and the warmth of their cabins with us. Jan always left a few coins on the table as was customary.

When darkness fell we spent the night with a Jewish family who gave us hot tea and a place to sleep. The following day we made it to Baligrod, Jan cursing every step of the way. When I entered the doctor's office, the warmth hit me in the face and I fainted. When I came around, my finger had already been operated on. The doctor said my passing out had been very opportune since he had no anesthetic.

I was exhausted so Jan grudgingly conceded to stop in a tavern and inquire about a place to stay. The tavern was full of German soldiers who kept staring at Tania and me. The bartender noticed this and signaled to his wife. She hurried forward and greeted us as if we were relatives and escorted us into the kitchen. She was a very kind woman and let us spend the night there next to the large brick oven.

The journey home was as difficult as the journey to Baligrod. Only I was more tired so we had to stop and rest more often. Our final stop was at a farmhouse with a thatched roof and two small windows covered with ice. The Ukrainian farmer invited us in and introduced his wife and son.

"I have only one son," he said. "My wife was not good enough to give me more. But he'll be getting married in the summer so maybe we'll have a lot of grandchildren."

Inside, the smell of freshly baked bread and boiling turnips filled the room. Ice was melting into a trickle of water on the earth floor. A kerosene lamp hung from a beam, lending a dim light to the religious pictures on the walls. There was a large fire burning in the brick oven that stood in the corner. The long table was covered with a white linen cloth, with benches on each side.

The farmer's wife set out some wooden spoons and a large bowl. Then she brought a steaming kettle of turnips to the table and poured some into the bowl along with some milk. Then the lady of the house finally spoke and invited her visitors to join them for dinner.

We sat down with great enthusiasm and started eating from the same bowl. The farmer slurped loudly and wiped his mouth on his embroidered sleeve but I was too hungry to mind. The fresh bread and hot turnip soup tasted wonderful.

When we finished, the farmer said a short prayer and everybody joined in. His son brought in a bundle of straw and spread it on the floor for us. Then the farmer, his wife and son climbed into the large bed. Everybody fell asleep almost immediately.

The next day I was able to complete the arduous journey in a cheerful mood despite Jan's constant grumbling and cursing. I was home at last and my finger was healing. At least he had taken me and stayed with me. That in itself was something. But then perhaps Tania had made the trip bearable for him. If so, then I was glad.

Chapter Nineteen

Spring arrived early in 1940, and with the warm winds, the snow quickly disappeared. I was feeling better and growing stronger every day. Jan didn't stay around the house very much. If he wasn't at work he was drinking and playing cards, but at this point I no longer cared.

I learned that Ivan was in Zatwarnica, working as a village clerk. I was also sure that he knew I was living there with my husband and son. I wanted to see him but not with a belly like a barrel. I would rather wait until summer when I would look nice again. Yet I hoped by some miracle that I would run into him. Instead I ran into Zbyshek.

"Ivan would like to see you," Zbyshek said.

"I have too many problems," I said. "Mitchel's sick. My husband's drinking heavily and making my life miserable. Tell Ivan I can't see him right now."

"I can't tell Ivan anything," Zbyshek said. "I've been inducted into the German army."

"The German army? But why?"

"My father's of German descent. They said that makes me a German and I have to fight for Germany."

"That's stupid," I said. "You're a Pole. You were born as a Pole. You grew up as a Pole."

"That may be true but if I don't go they'll send me to jail, and I'd rather be a soldier than a prisoner. So I'm leaving tomorrow. God knows where they'll send me."

"I thought the war was over."

"It is here in Poland, but Germany's still fighting France and England. Maybe I'll get to see Paris."

"What about your married lover?"

"I'm going to miss her," Zbyshek said. "I may never get to see her again but I suppose that's our destiny. We can't change that, can we."

"No," I said wistfully. "We can't."

� ✻ ✻

One evening in May, Jan came home to get more money for cards. He had gambled away his watch and every penny he had.

"I don't have any more money," I said.

A fury came over him and he slapped my face so hard I fell to the floor. Then he grabbed a butcher knife, knelt on my chest and pointed the knife at my throat.

"Where's the money?" he shouted. "I want the money!"

At that moment my father came in the door. When he saw what was going on he rushed in, grabbed Jan by the throat and lifted him off me.

"You no-good bastard!" he said. "I once said I could kill you like a snake. You weren't worth killing then and you're not worth killing now. But if you ever touch my daughter again, I won't hesitate!"

He shoved Jan away and sat down, flushed and breathing heavily. Jan scurried out of the house and I picked myself up off the floor. I went over to my father who was clutching his chest.

"My God," he said, looking up at me with tears in his eyes. "What have I done to my child?"

He took me in his arms and held me for a long time. Still clutching his chest, he got up and walked slowly out of the apartment. I stood in the kitchen, flooded in tears. I was afraid for my father and frightened of my husband, fearing that he would come back and kill me in my sleep. But two days passed before Jan came back, and when he did he never mentioned the incident. He was even polite for a short time.

⬛ ⬛ ⬛

In June, I began getting ready for the arrival of my second child. Mitchel was still sick and very cranky but I couldn't help him. There were no doctors and no medicine. We both had to suffer. I went to bed early because I wasn't feeling good, but Jan shaved and was getting ready to go out for the evening.

"Please don't go out tonight," I pleaded. "I don't feel so good and Mitchel is crying."

Jan laughed.

"I'm not going to stay home because Mitchel's crying," he said. "As for you, you never feel good. So I'm going to see some people who do."

He slammed the door behind him and was gone.

I fell asleep but woke up in the middle of the night because the bed was wet. A sharp pain was twisting my back. I looked around but Jan was nowhere to be seen.

"My God," I said. "The baby's coming and I'm all alone!"

I tried to get up to call for help but couldn't. The pain was too severe. I lay back down and the pain eased. In a few minutes the pain returned only this time it was much worse. I felt intense pressure and pushed. All of a sudden the baby came out and the pain was gone.

I lay there, shaking from fright. Slowly, I lifted the covers and looked at my baby. He was big and beautiful. I tore off a piece of bed sheet with my teeth and tied the umbilical cord. Then I waited and after another push the afterbirth came out. I was now free to get out of bed.

I dragged myself to the table, found the scissors, returned to the bed and cut the cord. I removed the dirty sheets from the bed, cradled the baby in my arms and lay back down. I knew somebody would come soon. Mother knew the baby was on its way and usually came herself or sent one of the younger children to check on me every morning. Finally Mother did arrive but she showed little emotion. She cleaned the baby first, and then me.

"What will you call him?" she asked.

I looked down at the baby and stroked his red cheek.

"Wiluis will be his name," I said. "And I shall call him Val."

"Does your husband agree?"

"I don't care if he does," I said firmly.

When Mother was finished she took Mitchel home with her and left me and the baby to fall asleep in each other's arms. Later, when I awoke, Jan was home and fixing himself something to eat. He came up to the bed and looked at the baby.

"Nice boy," he said.

"Yes he is," I said. "But where were you when I needed you?"

Jan snorted. "You didn't expect me to sit with you, did you? That's woman's work."

Two months later I was a healthy young woman again, slim and good-looking. My skin was clear, my cheeks were rosy and my breasts were full. My body was aching for love, but not for my husband.

Chapter Twenty

*I*t was a beautiful summer evening. I left the children with my parents and went for a stroll through town. Misty fog had settled over the ground and crickets had started their concert. It was all very peaceful. Nearly a year had passed since the Germans had invaded Poland. War and violence seemed far away.

I was walking through a part of the village where I seldom went when I heard voices and laughter coming from a big shadow of a house enshrouded in fog. I heard footsteps, many footsteps, and saw Mayor Kochut come out of the mist. A young man was with him. He looked to be young because he was stepping lightly and carrying his jacket over his shoulder. As they came closer, my heart stopped.

"My God," I gasped. "It's Ivan!"

Ivan saw me and stopped. The mayor smiled, tipped his cap and walked on.

"Victoria," Ivan said taking my hand. "You have no idea how desperately I've been trying to see you." He kissed my hand. "Why have you been avoiding me?"

I felt his eyes on me. His voice was gentle but his fiery looks were penetrating. My head spun. I lowered my eyes.

"I haven't been avoiding you," I said. "It's just that my son was sick, and I didn't go anywhere all winter."

We walked slowly without saying anything for a long time. We didn't have to. It felt good to be strolling side by side, the way normal lovers do. Suddenly Ivan spun me around and took me in his arms. I didn't protest. I let him hold me, my heart pounding wildly. Finally in his arms! I had been longing for them and now I fell into them like a lost child.

Ivan kissed my forehead, my eyes, my face, and put his lips on mine, gently. Then he pressed them hard with all his passion and desire. His hands trembled around my body. I closed my eyes and went limp, lost in a sweet faint.

"Victoria, I love you," he said. "I need you and long for you. Be mine and let me love you. I know Jan has your body. He's your husband. But your heart and soul belong to me."

My heart was full of joy.

"I love you too, Ivan," I said with a trembling voice.

"Then meet me tomorrow afternoon," he said. "Anywhere you say."

I looked at him all confused. Thoughts flew through my head like spooked birds. But my heart made the decision for me.

"Remember that meadow where we met on my grandfather's estate?" I asked.

"Remember?" he laughed. "How could I forget!"

"Wait for me there."

He kissed my hand and showered me with kisses.

"Good night, my love," he whispered. "Until tomorrow, my sweetest, sweetest love!"

He melted into the fog. I touched my lips where his lips had been. I still felt the taste of them, still smelled his presence and felt his arms around me.

"I can't believe I saw him!" I said to myself. "Was it a dream?" But then I grew solemn. I had let him hold me and kiss me. That was a sin, but I loved it! Oh my God, what was I to do? I wanted his love yet I knew it was forbidden. Forbidden to be with a man I love, but not forbidden to be with a man I hate. Who made this law?

I sat down on a bench and put my face on my knees. Burning tears filled my eyes. Pain seized my heart. My soul was tormented. I was being torn between a longing for love and the ultimate fear of committing a terrible sin. After a long struggle with myself, peace suddenly came. I stood up and wiped the tears from my eyes.

"I'll go!" I said. "I don't care about my husband, my children or my religion. I was deprived of love, cheated by God and my parents. Why was such a curse visited upon me? I was a good girl who never did anything wrong. I never hurt anyone. I suffered an unjust punishment, for what? I will steal my happiness. I will steal love. I will fulfill my desires with a man I love. If only for a moment or an hour, I can give him my heart."

When I arrived at the meadow, it was as if someone had put a wall around it to make a haven for lovers. It was covered with wildflowers and surrounded by young trees. The sun was high in a very blue sky and a chorus of birds was giving the most beautiful concert.

I threw myself onto the grass and spread my arms. Waiting here for my beloved made me so very happy. I caressed the little flowers around me. The whole world was smiling and the flowers were winking back at me. I heard footsteps and stood up. Through the leaves I saw Ivan running toward me. He came closer, lifted a branch and stood before me, his cheeks red from running, his chest heaving gently. He opened his arms and I fell into them.

"I've never seen you like this before," he said. "You're as fresh as a summer breeze. You smell like the flowers in the meadow."

He found my lips and we united in a sweet, long kiss.

"I love you, I love you, I love you!" he said as he picked me up and circled around joyfully. "Thank you for being here."

He put me down on the grass and lay next to me. I opened my arms, waiting for his love. He kissed my eyes and face, and pressed his lips on mine with crushing dominance. Waves of hot blood surged through me and I returned his kisses. He unbuttoned my dress and buried his face in my bosom. Then he touched me with a tender caress and covered me with his strong body. He took me.

I fell into sweet ecstasy as I received his love. It was the most precious gift sent to me from Heaven. Reward had come for my pain and my burning tears. This was the first time I had made love with a man I loved. I felt supreme pleasure I had never known before. I was hungry for it, and now that the glorious feeling was here, I didn't want it to stop. When Ivan rested, I held him close for fear the pleasure would escape me. I wanted him more, and he made love to me again. Feeling his body in mine, I felt safe. He was mine and I wanted him to stay in me forever.

"If there's a better place to make love than under the open blue sky," I said, "then lovers don't know the glory of it."

I kissed him again and tears rolled down my cheeks like rain on a very thirsty earth. He started to wipe them away but I restrained his hand and kissed it.

"Let them flow," I said. "These are tears of happiness from the happiest woman on earth. My heart and body belong to you. You're my life and my world."

"And you're mine," Ivan said. "But when will I see you again? I miss you already."

"I'll come tomorrow, and the day after tomorrow, and every day of my life. I will love you forever, Ivan. You'll be the only man in my life as long as I live, I promise."

I kissed him again and then got up and ran home. On the way I started to sing. I hadn't sung since I couldn't remember when. My heart was bursting with love. Sweet, sweet love, and I was blessed with it! I wished I could tell somebody. I wished I could share my happiness. But then I remembered.

I would have to come up with a good explanation for where I'd been. But did I really care what anybody said? No! I was so happy I could have told the world about my love and not cared what happened later. If I had died the next day I would have taken with me the happiness of that love.

When I got home I went into the bathroom and looked at myself in the mirror. I unbuttoned my dress, pulled it open the way Ivan had and examined my body. My breasts were full, creamy and voluptuous. My skin was smooth. I was content with what I saw. I was a woman now, a woman in love.

Chapter Twenty-One

It was a beautiful August morning, cool after the night's rain. A light breeze brought the aroma of fresh drying hay from the meadows where the workers had scythed the grass. From my apartment window I could see them eating their breakfast and watching the sky, judging if it would be sunny enough to dry the hay in one day.

My younger sister Emily came running up the steps and knocked on the door. Father was sick, Emily said, and Mother needed help.

"German soldiers were trying to drown a Jew in the ditch," she said, "and Daddy tried to stop them."

"Did they beat Daddy?"

"No," Emily said. "He collapsed from the struggle."

I left the children with a neighbor and ran as quickly as I could. At the house I found my mother bent over my father. He was lying on the bed, gasping for air.

"Jan, talk to me!" Mother said and shook him. "Open your eyes!"

I approached the bed and stood there in stunned disbelief. I had never seen my tall and robust father so helpless. It made me feel small and vulnerable.

"Jan, breathe!" Mother said. "Please don't die! You can't die and leave us here alone!"

Father struggled to open his mouth. His body convulsed. He opened his eyes and looked at his family. Then his eyes stood still and he stopped breathing. Mother let out a cry and dropped her head on his chest.

"Jan, why did you go and leave us here alone?" she sobbed. "And for what? They drowned the Jew anyway! Now what's going to happen to us?"

My sisters started to weep quietly. My brothers cried too, but I couldn't cry. I was still in shock.

Even at the graveside I was unable to cry. As the coffin was lowered into the grave, I stared into the deep hole. Jan moved close to me but I didn't see him or hear him. I saw only the freshly dug earth that was being thrown into my father's grave. Bang bang. The dirt and stones kept hitting the coffin. Father was going to be so deep under that pile of dirt. It was going to be so heavy on him. He would be lying there forever and I would never see him again.

Suddenly my knees bent and I fell to the ground like a cut flower.

※　　※　　※

I spent many hours staring out the window, thinking about my father. But then I remembered all the beautiful and happy moments I had spent with him and a smile crossed my face.

"Daddy, I love you," I said to his memory. "I was very hurt when you forced me to marry Jan Hertig, but I forgave you a long time ago. I wish I had told you so you'd know I'm not angry with you. You have to hear me, Daddy, and somehow let me know that you understand. This is the end of my confession, and the end of this chapter in my life. I have to close my diary on you, but you'll stay in my heart forever."

During that period of mourning, I locked Jan out of my life. I didn't speak to him, and when he tried to make conversation I barely replied. He was irritated by that but was unable to pick a fight with me because I refused to respond to him in any way.

"You don't care if I'm home or not," he grumbled. "You don't care if I'm drunk or not. What's going to happen to us? How are we going to live when you're not speaking?"

"I don't care what you do," I said and went back to my silence.

It was exactly one month to the day of my father's death when I saw him standing in my mother's garden. He was so real, so alive, I forgot that he was dead. I ran up to him, skipping the two steps that led into garden, and stood before him.

"Daddy, you came back to us!" I said. "We love you." I stretched my arms out to him. "Come back to us, please."

He looked at me with his beautiful loving eyes, a big smile on his face. He made a motion with his head meaning no, that he couldn't, and disappeared before my eyes. I stood there holding my arms outstretched as though I wanted to catch him but he was gone. I looked where he had been standing and peace came over me. He had sent this peace to me.

"Daddy, I know you love us," I said. "I know you're watching over us. Nothing bad will ever happen to us because you're always with us."

I couldn't see him anymore but I knew he was still there. The tall dahlias where he stood were moving back and forth, yet there was no wind.

Chapter Twenty-Two

A woman in love is the most beautiful woman on earth. She is radiant, like a flower in the morning sun, and her happiness is written all over her. A dreamy haze covers her eyes and a happy smile is on her beautiful lips, making dimples in her rosy cheeks.

I was seeing Ivan every chance I got, and each time was like the first time. Every kiss of his made up for every painful slap of my husband's. Jan was drinking heavily. When he got drunk he demanded his husband's rights. When I refused he became blind with rage and beat me unmercifully. But I wouldn't let his abuse cloud my love for Ivan. I suffered quietly, thinking only of Ivan's kisses, and the pain fled from my body and soul.

Ivan was now village clerk for about thirty villages. To the great delight of his father, Ivan was a very powerful and respected man in the region. His father arranged a marriage for him with an attractive Ukrainian girl, but he did it without telling Ivan. That angered Ivan and caused him to move out of the house. Ivan took a small apartment above his office which made it very convenient for us.

I had stars in my eyes knowing that Ivan loved me, and my God, how I loved him. I didn't see the war going on around me and didn't see the blood that was being spilled on every inch of my land. I saw only Ivan's eyes.

❖ ❖ ❖

A quota was set by the Germans for each village to send teenage boys and girls to Germany. They were to take the places in the factories of those who had been called to the armed forces. Mayor Kochut had the authority to decide who would go and selected one of my brothers and one of my sisters to fill the quota. Mother begged him not to send them away.

"Your children are older and they're not going!" she said in torment.

"My orders are to send only Polish kids," the mayor said callously. "No Ukrainians or Jews. Just be glad they're not Jews."

Mother decided then and there that she and the children would have to leave Poland. She wrote to Grandfather for help but it was already too late. The German-appointed Ukrainian police were going from house to house, rounding up the youngsters.

I arrived just as my brother and sister were being taken away. They were crying, terror contorting their sweet young faces as the police dragged them out of Mother's arms. Mother fell to the ground in desolate grief and covered her head with her arms.

"My poor children," she sobbed when I tried to raise her up. "The fear in their eyes—I'll never forget it! God knows what will happen to them, and I can't help them! Oh

Jan, why did you have to die and leave us at the mercy of God?"

Crying filled other Polish homes as teenagers were separated from weeping parents. They were taken to the police station and put on trucks. Then the Ukrainian police escorted the trucks to a train that would take them to Germany.

The travel documents arrived a few days later and Mother showed them to me.

"Come with me," she said excitedly. "You can travel as your sister. Mitchel and Val can go as your brothers. We can take a train from Baligrod and be in Vienna next week. You can tell your husband you're taking a short vacation. I'm sure he won't stop you."

"Mommy, calm down," I said. "I'll have to think about it. The Germans aren't stupid, you know. I don't want to expose us to danger."

"There's more danger here," Mother said. "I'll arrange for transportation to Baligrod while you think it over. But please, make a good decision and come with me."

I went to the cemetery. It was a very cold and dreary March day. Snow still covered the ground, revealing only wooden crosses on mounds that marked the graves. I knelt down where my father was buried and said a prayer. Then I stood up.

"Daddy, are you cold under all this snow?" I asked the frozen grave as if I was talking to my father. "If you are, you can tell me. You can tell me everything about the world you live in now. Perhaps it's a better world than this one. In this world we have too much worry and fear. Especially me."

I brushed the snow from a cross so his name was visible.

"Mother wants me to go to Vienna with her and leave my husband behind," I said. "I'd go, only something's holding me here. Or should I say someone. It isn't Jan. Him I could leave anytime. It's Ivan that I can't leave. I love him, Daddy, and he loves me. I can't think for a moment that I could leave him and not be close to him for a long time. That would kill me. I'd rather not live at all than live without him. My feelings for Ivan are stronger than my fears of the danger closing in on us. So I'll stay, and tell mother of my decision."

I knelt down and pushed the snow away from the grave. I lowered my face to the cold frozen earth and kissed it. A noise behind me caused me to look around. Ivan was standing there.

"How long have you been here?" I asked, surprised.

"Long enough to hear you tell your father how much you love me," he said. He helped me to my feet and held me close. "I'm sorry for the pain you're bearing over your father's death. I love you so, it breaks my heart to see you sad and suffering."

"Ivan, I feel lonely and afraid," I said. "My father's not here to protect me, and if my mother leaves I'll be left alone. My mother wants me to go with her but I can't leave you. What am I to do?"

"You must accept that your father is no longer here and bury the hurt," Ivan said. "But I'm here. I'd rather die a hundred times than let the slightest harm come to you. I'll love you and protect you, Victoria. Remember that."

He lifted my hands to his lips and kissed them.

"I have a political meeting to attend," he said. "Come and see me tonight. I'll wait for you, my darling."

Ivan left, and I went straight to my mother's house.

"I've decided to stay," I told her.

She looked stricken.

"You'll suffer if you stay," she said. "You'll be here all alone and you'll die here. No one will help you, my daughter. Please, change your mind. I'm begging you."

I was unmoved.

"I'll not die here," I said emphatically. "And I'm not alone. I have a husband and two sons."

I took the children to see Mother off. Jan did not come with us. He had said his cursory farewell the night before. Mother was sniffing and wiping her eyes as she kissed me and my children goodbye.

"There's still time for you to come," she said.

"Don't worry, Mommy, we'll be safe," I said as I watched my mother climb into the horse-drawn wagon with my youngest brother and sister. "Write to me. Maybe I'll come to Vienna later."

I held my babies tightly and watched the wagon drive off. Mother turned and waved. Mitchel waved his little hand back at her.

※　　※　　※

One afternoon, before going to meet Ivan, I put a cold compress on my face. It was swollen and red from a beating Jan had given me. The compress helped but the bruises still showed. I thought about not going but couldn't bear to disappoint Ivan or myself.

"What happened to you?" Ivan asked with suspicion and concern when he saw my face. "Did your husband hit you? I have to know."

"Yes," I said quietly. "But it's all right. Honestly it is."

"No it isn't!" he said angrily. "If he hits you again I'll kill him!" He stroked my battered cheek. "Does he know about us? Is that why he beat you?"

"No Ivan, he doesn't know of my love for you."

"Then why?"

I turned away.

"He wants to make love to me but I can't do it," I said. "I let him before, before I learned what real love was all about. But now that I've discovered sweet lovemaking with you, I can't let him touch me. That makes him angry and he beats me. He even hurt me before we were married, and I'll never forgive him for the pain and agony he put me through."

"What do you mean, before you were married?" Ivan asked.

I sat on the bed beside him.

"I have to tell you something you have a right to know," I said. "Be strong. It's past and I don't want you to be angry. Promise me."

Ivan's face changed. He stared at me blankly as if he was afraid to hear what I was going to say. As I talked, his jaw moved intensely but he listened in silence.

"When you asked me why I married Jan Hertig, I told you my parents forced me," I said caressing his face. "That was true. But there was a reason for it. You see, my dearest, Jan Hertig raped me and my father made him marry me. I think he did that to punish Jan, not knowing he was punishing me instead."

Ivan dropped his face into his hands.

"My God!" he said through welling tears. "I blamed you! I cursed you! How could I have done that? Forgive me, Victoria!"

"There's nothing to forgive, my darling."

"If I had only known! I would have killed him!"

I could see that a horrible battle was being waged in Ivan's heart. Anger sparkled in his eyes.

"I'm telling you now that Hertig will pay for his crime," he said. "So help me God."

"He's already paying," I said. "He knows I don't love him and never will. That'll be his punishment for the rest of his life."

Later, after we made love, Ivan spoke softly.

"Listen carefully," he said. "I have to tell you something very important."

I lifted my eyes up to him. When I was with him I felt safe and secure.

"There's going to be another war," he said. "This time between the Germans and Russians. We'll be caught between two monsters, and there will be a lot of bloodshed in these mountains."

"How do you know this?" I asked.

"I know. You must take your baby and go to a safe place, to Vienna with your mother and grandparents."

"I can't leave you," I started to say.

Ivan put his hand on my lips.

"Hush, my love. Listen to what I have to say. If you stay, you'll be in great danger, not only from the Germans and Russians, but from my people too."

"Your people? I don't understand."

"I can't tell you any more. I've already told you too much. I've taken an oath to work for the Ukrainian homeland, and I swore not to speak of this to anyone."

I stared at him, trying to understand.

"I'll go only if you go with me," I said. "We'll take my sons and go to Vienna where we can live together. Otherwise I'm staying here."

"But you can't stay here! You have to go! I'm ordering you!"

"I'll never leave you," I said. "If I'm to die, I'll die here with you because I can't live without you. If danger comes, I know you will protect me."

Ivan took me in his arms and smiled at me.

"Nothing on this earth will ever separate you from me," he said. "Nothing."

Chapter Twenty-Three

*I*n June of 1941, at dawn, a roar like thunder shook the Carpathian Mountains. Jan and I jumped out of bed and ran outside to look at the sky with the rest of the frightened villagers. Squadrons of low-flying planes were coming from the south.

"German bombers," Jan said.

The planes flew over the River San and continued on into Russian-occupied Poland.

"It looks like the Germans have finally turned on the Russians," Jan said. "So now we have a new war."

Watching the planes fly by, I recalled what Ivan had told me.

"We will be caught between two monsters," he had said. "And there will be a lot of bloodshed in these mountains."

Jan waited until he was sure there was no fighting in the area and went to Lutowiska.

"The Russians are gone," he said when he came back. "And so is everything I own. No furniture, no lights, no doors. Only two windows in the house remain unbroken and the shop's been looted. If you had stayed there as you were supposed to, we'd have a house and a business to go back to. After all my hard work I'm ruined, thanks to you!"

I didn't say a word. I picked up the children and walked out of the apartment. This made Jan even angrier and he went back to Lutowiska to make repairs. When the house was liveable he came back for us.

"It's time for you to move to Lutowiska with me," he said. "We have to start living a normal life."

I hesitated. I was caught off guard, with no chance to say anything to Ivan.

"I'll come next week," I started to say.

But Jan grabbed my shoulders and squeezed hard.

"Pack," he said. "You're coming with me now."

I did as I was told but insisted we stop and see how my Uncle Leon and his family were doing. We found the house in a little village on the north side of the San but nobody was inside.

"The Russians are worse than a plague of locusts," Jan said. "They stripped away everything."

"It's not the contents I'm worried about," I said with a heavy heart. "My relatives used to live here."

We continued on to Lutowiska and pulled up in front of the house. When Mrs. Friedes saw us, she gathered her daughters and brought over some cookies and fresh coffee. My face shone and I embraced them each in turn.

"Thank God I found a new family since I lost mine," I said. I told Mrs. Friedes everything and then asked, "How did everybody survive the Russians?"

Mrs. Friedes shook her head in sorrow.

"Petrusia was able to get away to the farm where her mother lives," she said. "But the Catholic priest has disappeared. The pharmacist and city attorney are missing. Dr. Schreiber, Judge Puchalski and their families have vanished without a trace. And they hanged the public prosecutor from a tree in the middle of town. They left him there for three days."

"My God!" I said. "How awful!"

"People have stopped talking to one another, afraid they might say something to incriminate themselves. Nobody trusts anybody."

"How are the Landows?"

"Mr. Landow was arrested by the Russians and taken away. Nobody knows where."

"Oh my God, no!" I said. "And Sheila?"

"Gone too."

"Gone?" I asked fearfully.

"Ran away with a few hundred Jews when she heard the Germans were coming. They say she had a plan to go to Palestine. That's all I can tell you."

"God bless her," I said. "Sheila's a clever woman. Whatever plan she has, I'm sure it'll work."

Mrs. Friedes leaned forward and patted my hand.

"It's good you weren't here. God knows what might have happened to you and the children."

◈　　◈　　◈

I tried to make the house as comfortable as possible under the circumstances, but the lack of furniture made that almost impossible. So I left the children with Mrs. Friedes and hired a man with a wagon to take me to Zatwarnica. We went directly to my Grandfather's estate and knocked on the front door of the house.

Mayor Kochut opened the door and frowned down on me.

"Can I help you?" he asked, annoyed at the intrusion.

"I'm here to take some of my grandfather's furniture," I said. "With your permission, of course. The Russians left us nothing when they evacuated Lutowiska."

"The Russians are pigs," the mayor said. "When the Germans moved on, they instructed me to move in here as guardian of the estate, which you can see I have done. Now they're sending me to Lutowiska so you can take what you need. There's no one else of stature who merits living here."

I went inside and looked around. Where once the house was full of happy people and laughter, it was now nearly empty and as cold as a morgue. I selected what I needed and told the driver to load it all on the wagon while I went into the village.

I went straight to Ivan's apartment and knocked on the door. No answer. I tried the door. Locked. My hopes sagged and I turned to leave when I heard footsteps coming up the stairs two at a time. It was Ivan!

"I saw you come up here," he said and swept me into his arms.

He kissed me fiercely and then led me into the apartment. He closed the door behind us and locked it.

"I have to love you today, now!" he said. "I can't wait. My blood is boiling!"

His desire overwhelmed him and he lifted me onto the bed. He lay next to me, kissing me and undressing me at the same time. When he saw my nude body he took me with desire and hunger, making love to me like never before. After hours of passionate and then quiet lovemaking, we lay in each other's arms. We didn't speak. We had many moments like this. We knew what the other was thinking. We needed no words.

Ivan broke the silence by whispering in my ear.

"Victoria, my love, I have to tell you something very important."

I didn't open my eyes and didn't move. I only pressed my face closer to him.

"I love you with all my heart," he said. "You are my love and my happiness in this dreadful world. But—"

I raised my head and looked into his eyes.

"—I have to leave you," he said.

I froze.

"Not forever," he continued. "I was called to duty by the Ukrainian partisans. I have to obey orders. Do you understand?"

I didn't answer. My body started to shake with sobs. Tears flowed from my eyes and fell on his chest. He held my face in his hands and kissed the tears away.

"Don't cry, my sweetheart. I'll come back to you soon."

"No Ivan, you won't," I said through sobs. "I know I'll never see you again. People are being killed every day in this ugly war. If you go, you'll be killed too."

"But I won't," he said. "I'll do everything in my power to stay alive so I can see you and love you again."

"If you must go, take me with you," I said. "I'll walk with you, sleep with you, eat what you eat, drink what you drink—"

"I can't take you with me," Ivan said. "There's no place for a woman. My life will be much happier knowing there's a young woman waiting for me who loves me. I'll carry you in my heart wherever I go. We won't be apart for a moment."

After we got dressed Ivan took me in his arms for the last time.

"Goodbye, my sweet love," he said, his voice starting to break. "Let's not think about tomorrow, let's think about today. Today belongs to us. We can love each other now and forget tomorrow. We'll take our happiness when it's given to us. One precious hour of love will make up for a thousand empty days."

I broke loose from his embrace and ran out the door. I ran through town, my face overflowing with tears. People turned their heads to look at me but I didn't care. My heart was shattered. It would never be the same again.

❋   ❋   ❋

In Lutowiska, Mr. Friedes came to visit. He looked troubled so I made a pot of tea and set out a tray of biscuits. He ate them greedily and apologized for doing so.

"Food is scarce for everyone," he said, "but if you're a Jew it doesn't exist. Most of the ration stamps went to Ukrainians, and some to Poles, but Jews got none."

"The Germans are behind this," Jan said.

Mr. Friedes nodded. "Not only them. When the Russians left, the Germans installed a Ukrainian mayor."

"Kochut," I said. "We know him from Zatwarnica. He's not such a bad man."

"By his deeds shall you know him," Mr. Friedes said. "He appointed a new police chief from the Ukraine called Hoculak. People tremble at the sight of the man even though he's only thirty-five. He's tall and handsome with dark curly hair but he has a sinister face. He's polite to a fault, and brutal."

"I've heard of him," I said. "He's part of Bandera's group."

"Bandera!" Jan said and stared at me in amazement. "How do you know all this?"

I shrugged. "Rumors."

"Last week, Hoculak's police searched Jewish houses for firearms," Mr. Friedes said. "But they took everything else they could lay their hands on—jewelry, clothes, dishes, and especially our food. We tried to buy more food but Poles don't have much to begin with, and Ukrainians won't sell to us." He brightened slightly. "Ukrainian farmers will, however. Outside of town, a new pair of shoes buys ten eggs, and a Persian lamb coat gets fifty pounds of potatoes."

"I can't believe the police are being allowed to commit crimes like that," Jan said. "This riffraff has power. God knows how they will use it next."

"In all humility, I know too," Mr. Friedes said. "Kochut's planning to confiscate all Jewish property—our stores, land and livestock."

"That's outrageous," I said. "Can we do anything to help?"

Mr. Friedes drew his chair up close.

"I have a big piece of land with potatoes growing on it," he said. "Enough to feed all the Jews in Lutowiska through the winter. What if I signed this land over to you?"

Jan stood up and started to pace the floor.

"I don't know if we can get away with that," he said. "By now, the mayor must know who owns what."

"He hasn't finished his inquiries yet," Mr. Friedes said. "There's still time to make out the necessary papers."

"A good idea but risky," Jan said. "Who's going to make them out? They'll have to look like they were signed before the war."

"If you agree, I can take care of that," Mr. Friedes said. "And you will save every Jew in town from starvation."

Jan was quiet. He was thinking. I knew he was reluctant to take a risk like this.

"I have a better idea," I said. "Sign the land over to me. We can make it look like it was a wedding present from my grandfather."

"That's not only a better idea, it's safer too!" Jan said, glad that his skin would not be involved. He turned to me. "Sometimes you can be pretty smart."

"Very smart," Mr. Friedes said with a sigh of relief. He stood up and shook Jan's hand. "Thank you for helping us." He turned to me and kissed my hand. "My blessing on you, my child, and on your house."

Chapter Twenty-Four

Gusts of chilly winds drifted through the mountains. Oak and maple trees were adorned in gold and scarlet. It was the fall of 1941, and the time had come to harvest the fields of potatoes.

I opened a dresser drawer and took out a creased document. I put it in my purse, left the children with Mrs. Friedes and went to the mayor's office in the rectory of the Catholic church. I paused at the church door and recalled that wonderful Christmas Eve service with its smiling faces and happy voices. On impulse I went inside and knelt in a pew.

"God, what are you going to do with us?" I prayed. "Why are the Jews being persecuted? You let them be stripped of dignity and pride, of their possessions and food by hoodlums. How can they live without food? What's going on, God? They pray to you as no one ever prayed before. Do you hear them? Do you hear me? Or have you shut your ears to our cries and prayers, and closed your eyes to the suffering? Did you send Hoculak to Lutowiska? He's a satan from hell. We're so afraid of him. Good Jesus, take him away from Lutowiska, and this misfortune away from us."

I walked over to the rectory and went into the mayor's office. He gave me an unfriendly look.

"Oh, it's you," Kochut grumbled. "What do you want this time?"

"I own twenty acres of farm land," I said. "Potatoes are growing there and I have no way of knowing who planted them. I need your permission to harvest them."

He looked at me with suspicion. "You want to harvest potatoes you didn't plant? How do I know the land belongs to you?"

I took the deed out of my purse and put it on his desk. Kochut picked it up and examined it. My heart started to pound and blood rushed to my face. I could feel my courage draining away. Kochut gave the deed back to me.

"You can harvest the potatoes," he said. "But you have to deliver half to my warehouse. An assessment by the German government, you know. It's the new law."

With trembling hands, I slipped the deed into my purse.

"One more thing," I said.

"And what is that?" Kochut asked harshly.

"If I hoe the potatoes myself, I won't get them up in time to avoid the frost."

"What's wrong with your husband?"

"He works long hours as a lumberjack in the forest. Would it be possible to take Jews to the fields and put them to work? They have nothing to do anyway."

I waited, scared stiff, while Kochut studied me.

"You're a very beautiful woman," he said. "I can understand why your husband protects you so stubbornly."

"And the Jews?" I asked.

"Yes, yes, take them. But don't let them steal any potatoes from you. Even worse, don't give them any. You'll be punished for breaking the law."

Once outside, I ran home as though I was being chased by a pack of wolves. I gladdened the hearts of the Friedes by telling them the good news, and waited anxiously for Jan to come home. He had barely stepped through the door before I blurted it all out. I was especially proud of the clever way I had connived to get help for the Jews.

"Good," Jan said with admiration. "I'll be able to help on weekends when I'm not tied to this miserable job. The Germans denied my request to reopen the tobacco store even though they're letting Zawacki reopen his liquor store."

"First things first," I said with a smirk. "Were you able to find a cow? Or will the children have to drink vodka too?"

"A cow and some chickens," Jan said. "I couldn't have gotten them without Zawacki. The man certainly has connections."

※　　※　　※

I was working in the field hoeing potatoes with the Friedes and two other Jewish families. The baskets were being quickly filled and emptied into large sacks. Then the full sacks were carefully stacked while we waited for Jan to show up with a horse-drawn wagon. I straightened up to rest my back when I heard a honking sound from overhead.

"Look!" I said to the others. "Wild geese flying south."

"They're lucky," one of the Friedes girls said. "They have wings and can fly away when winter and hunger approach. I wish I could fly with them, to a faraway world where there's peace, sunshine, happiness and food, plenty of food."

With her chapped hands she stroked away the tears that were forming and returned to her work.

"Here comes the wagon!" Mr. Friedes said pointing to the far side of the field.

Jan drove up with Mr. Zawacki at his side. I exhibited surprise at Zawacki's presence.

"Zawacki's a good man," Friedes reassured me. "He helps supply Sheila Landow with provisions for her hiding place."

"Sheila has a hiding place?" I asked suddenly alert. "Where?"

"In the Carynskie forest," Friedes said. "That's all I can say."

Jan stood up in the wagon. "Listen! Zawacki has something to say."

Everybody stopped what they were doing and turned to listen.

"Don't take all the potatoes home," Zawacki said. "And whatever you do, don't take the full share to Kochut's warehouse. He doesn't deserve them." He spat in contempt. "Hide them here in the field, under ground. We'll smuggle them out at night."

The others nodded in agreement.

"But we can't hide them in Jewish homes," Zawacki went on. "Hoculak would be sure to find them and give you big trouble. We'll have to find a safe place to store them. Agreed?"

Everybody exchanged glances and nods.

"Agreed!" Friedes said.

Work started fast. Women hoed the potatoes out of the ground while men dug deep holes and buried them. Sack after sack disappeared until at the end of the day only a few were left. These were loaded onto the wagon. Jan took half to Kochut's warehouse and the other half home. He said it gave him grim satisfaction to be able to cheat the cheaters.

The first snow covered the ground surrounding the mountain region with charm and tranquility. But in Lutowiska, bitter cold put its icy grip on Poles and Jews alike. Poles were allowed to go into the forest and gather firewood but Jews were not allowed to leave town. And Hoculak posted his men like Lucifer's police just to make sure.

I watched helplessly as the Friedes chopped up their furniture for fuel. At first they took only the oldest pieces, but when those were gone they took anything that would burn—chests, wardrobes, cabinets and beds.

When Dr. Shline came by to look after the Friedes, I naively asked him if he could give me anything for a bad cold. Dr. Shline threw up his hands.

"I have nothing for you or the Friedes," he said in despair. "Fever and pneumonia are raging everywhere. People are dying from cold and hunger and I can't help them. What little medicine the Germans give me can only be used on Ukrainians, and it all has to be accounted for."

"Maybe we can organize and stand up to them," I said. "Maybe somebody will kill Hoculak. I wish I could. If I was a man, maybe I'd be able to."

"Don't even think about it," Dr. Shline said. "Another will come along who's even worse."

"Then what are we to do? Where can we turn?"

Dr. Shline shook his head sorrowfully.

"I tried to contact my relatives in America," he said. "But I found out that letters from Jews are read at the post office and burned. We have nowhere to turn and nobody to ask for help except people like you who are suffering too. God bless you for it, Victoria, but be careful. Hunger puts no limits on jealousy. Give to one and not the other, and the other might report you."

I thanked Dr. Shline but paid no heed to his warning. I packed bread, milk, eggs and whatever else I could spare into the bottom of the baby carriage. I bundled up the children, put them on top and went for a stroll. I stopped at the Friedes house first and slipped them a package through the door. I did the same at other houses, all with great caution. My Jewish friends knew I was coming and waited for me by the door. Sometimes the Ukrainian police walked by but they never noticed anything suspicious. I too derived a grim satisfaction from cheating on the cheaters.

※　　※　　※

Christmas passed and New Year's Eve came, but there was no joy in Lutowiska. Only the Ukrainians were celebrating the coming of 1942. And it was a celebration far different from the ones I remembered. There was no music and no grand ball. There were no beautiful gowns and glittering jewelry, no elegantly dressed gentlemen. There was only the screaming of drunken Ukrainian police.

I was sitting in my dark living room watching the antics in the courtroom across the street when a horde of drunken revelers came staggering out the front door. They started cursing and shooting their guns, first into the air then everywhere. A bullet pierced the window where I was sitting and passed inches from my head. I ducked to the floor and crawled into the bedroom where Jan was sleeping. I marveled at how he was able to sleep through all kinds of chaos.

"Jan! Get up quickly!" I said. "They're shooting! We have to take the children and hide!"

Jan sprang out of bed and helped me move the children. We crawled into a corner and sheltered them with our bodies. We could hear the cracking of broken glass and the shrill laughter as if hell had released an army of devils.

"The bastards!" Jan said. "I wish I could stop them but I'm only one man!"

He cautiously looked out the window.

"What are you doing?" I said. "You'll get your head shot off!"

"They're smashing all the windows in the Friedes house with long wooden planks," he said. "Now they're headed into town."

A big new moon was shining through the window, carefree and unconcerned by the outrageous horror being inflicted by some people on other innocent ones.

"Dear Jesus!" I said, shivering from fright and cold. "Stop them! Please stop them!"

In the morning when peace was restored, I hurried to the Friedes house. They had covered the broken windows with blankets and mattresses to protect themselves from the deadly cold. Inside, it was dark and frigid. The family was huddled together on the couch under layers of blankets and coats.

"Look at us and remember what you see," Mrs. Friedes said. There was bitterness in her voice. "It's like this in every Jewish home."

I could say nothing. I knelt down beside the girls and stroked their hair with sorrow in my heart.

"I feel so humiliated and abused," Mrs. Friedes started to cry. "I wish they would just finish with this cruelty and take our lives. I can't take this any longer!"

Now the daughters started to cry.

"All right, ladies," Mr. Friedes said, trying very hard to look composed. "Stop being crybabies. So they broke our windows. So what? We'll fix them."

"And Jan will help," I said. "He's already looking for glass and boards. In the meantime the girls can come home with me and get some firewood."

"You're endangering yourself," Mr. Friedes said. "The police are watching."

"They'll pay no attention to the girls."

I led the girls back to my house by way of the garden and helped them load two sacks of wood. I sent them home one at a time with the sacks. Then I picked up some bread, milk and eggs and took them over myself.

"You'll feel better after a good breakfast," I said.

"God bless you, child!" Mrs. Friedes said. "How can we ever thank you?"

I smiled coyly. "When the war's over I'll send you a bill."

This brought a little cheer and hope to the Friedes family.

When I walked through town my horror grew. Houses that once were cozy and warm with the laughter of children now had rags covering their windows. Behind the doors I could hear the crying of children, the lamentations of women and the praying of men.

Mr. Zawacki came up to me, shaking his head.

"I told Hoculak this kind of behavior is criminal," he said. "As a Ukrainian he should be ashamed."

"What did he say?"

Zawacki snorted.

"He said his boys are good cops who happened to act a little crazy after a few drinks. And he wanted to know why was I so interested in protecting the Jews. Ha! If I knew how to protect them I would, but I'm powerless. Everybody's powerless. Hoculak and his thugs have guns while we have none. How can we fight that kind of evil?"

"We can help them survive," I said.

Zawacki smiled and winked.

"We've already started," he said. "I spoke to your husband and a few others who promised to help. We're going to replace all the windows that were broken. We'll help in other ways too. We're going to defeat this Hoculak, and the Jews are going to live. But God help us if Hoculak finds out."

Chapter Twenty-Five

*T*hat winter was the worst that people in the Carpathian Mountains had ever experienced. Jewish children now came out of their homes and into the streets of Lutowiska, their faces pale and thin. They didn't know what was going on, didn't understand why there was no food for them, and no wood to start a fire in their cold ovens. Through pitiful eyes they looked at people passing by. The children just stared, their thin bodies shaking from hunger and bitter cold, until merciful death ended their suffering. But there were no burials. No one had strength to take them to the cemetery and dig graves. Corpses were left in the snow in back yards or in the street until Hoculak ordered the Poles to pick them up and bury them.

I was taking some food in a baby carriage to Mrs. Landow when I passed a little boy and girl sitting in front of a house. Their faces were swollen and their bellies bloated, a sign of starvation. The little girl extended her hand and asked for bread. She was beautiful, with long curly blond hair, and blue eyes brimming with tears. I took some bread and milk out of the carriage and knocked on the door of the house. A tall pretty woman opened the door. She said nothing and only looked at me.

"For your children," I said and handed her the food.

The woman didn't answer. She took the food, ushered her children inside and closed the door. She was probably bewildered by this unexpected act of humanity. I knew she would thank God later, even though God had nothing to do with it.

I knocked on Mrs. Landow's back door but got no answer. The door was unlocked so I quickly rolled the carriage into the kitchen and locked the door behind me. Inside, it was dark and quiet. I walked through the house and into the bedroom where I found Mrs. Landow lying in bed.

"Mrs. Landow!" I said anxiously. "Are you sick?"

"My angel," Mrs. Landow said with a quiver in her voice. "Why do you bother to come and risk your life for me? I don't feel well so I have decided to stay in bed and die. There's nothing left to live for anyway."

"You have to live," I said. "Your husband will return, and so will Sheila. Don't you want to see her again?"

"My God, how I want to see her! I only hope she escaped and doesn't have to see the bestiality that surrounds us."

I went to the kitchen and kindled a fire. I heated the milk and took it in to Mrs. Landow with some bread.

"They say Sheila's hiding in the forest," I said. "Is that true?"

"I will tell you something for your ears only," Mrs. Landow said. "A secret you'll have to take to the grave."

"You can trust me," I said.

"After you ran away to Zatwarnica, Sheila invited her close friends to the house. If most of our people perish in this war, she said, they would have to be the ones to start a new generation. They are healthy and young so they can survive. But not here. Here they will die. They would have to find a safe place and survive for Israel."

"The Carynskie forest!" I said.

"Too many people know that much," Mrs. Landow said. "Sheila's living in the wilderness with a thousand Jews, maybe more. But only adults. Children and old people were not taken. Sheila said they would get sick and endanger the rest. Some quarreled with her over this and refused to leave their families behind, but most went."

"I could not have left my babies behind," I said.

"I insisted Sheila go without us," Mrs. Landow said. "Maybe nothing will happen to us. If we're taken to work camps we'll have a chance to survive. But we have to be absolutely sure that they will survive."

"How heroic," I said.

"Then the Russians came to the house. Sheila started the phonograph and everybody pretended to dance as if they were having a party. The officer said everybody was under arrest. We were *kulaks*, drinking the blood of the poor, and now it was our turn to bleed. My husband came into the room and said that they were not *kulaks* but Communists. How dare his own daughter hold a Communist meeting in his house! He pushed her roughly and scolded me for sympathizing. He said we were all a bunch of Reds."

"But you're not!" I said.

"Of course we're not," Mrs. Landow said. "The Russian soldiers believed him and took my poor husband away. There was great pain in his eyes as they led him out—and great love."

"Truly heroic," I said again.

I gathered up the dishes which had been wiped clean.

"Why don't we move a sofa into the kitchen?" I said. "It's the warmest room in the house and you can sleep there."

Mrs. Landow smiled and nodded.

"My child, your presence has restored my hope," she said. "I can live in one room, and I promise you that I will not wait for death. I'll wait for my family to come home to me."

※　※　※

Winter finally broke. Warm breezes swayed the pine trees in the forest. The ground was covered with white snow flowers. The fields swarmed with busy farmers working Mother Earth for a fresh food supply. Ukrainians in their colorful clothes brightened the big black patches of bare fields. But the festive singing and laughter of their children pierced Jewish and Polish hearts like a knife.

There were still potatoes left in our cellar and on Mr. Friedes's advice we cut each potato into three parts. That way we were able to plant the entire field.

"Food is growing for us again," Mr. Friedes said. "Perhaps we'll survive another winter. Although one or two more like this and we'll all perish. Then the Ukrainians can honestly say they didn't kill one Jew."

"I call it killing," I said. "Killing by starvation. Maybe I'll get permission to go to German headquarters in Sanok and report this inhuman policy."

"You think the Germans don't know?" Jan scoffed. "They gave Hoculak the power and he's doing their dirty work for them."

※　※　※

May, 1942. Beauty had enveloped the Carpathian Mountains. I went out on the porch and inhaled the aroma of blossoms. I could see gardens everywhere sprouting vegetables and flowers. Wheat, oats, rye and potatoes were blanketing the fields in different shades of green. Cattle were grazing in the meadows, and the forests were abuzz with romantic melodies.

All this beauty Nature gave to all people, yet not all people were able to enjoy it. What a contrast! The beauty of spring and the suffering of Jews. Their adversity and humiliation was unspeakable. Once a very proud and respected people, they were now forced to walk like beggars through back streets looking for scraps of food, or in empty fields looking for one potato. Discouraged and desolate, they were losing their will to live. God, I hoped this war would end soon or they would all die, not only from hunger but from the despair and degradation that was taking away their human dignity.

I started to go back inside when I saw a ragged beggar approaching. He was unshaven and his hair was long and dirty. I hesitated because I thought I recognized him.

"Uncle Leon?" I said. "Is that you?"

"It's good to be back," Uncle Leon said as he came up on the porch.

I embraced him and looked into his face.

"My God!" I cried. "You only have one eye!"

"And I'm tired and hungry," he said. "Do you have anything to eat?"

I rushed him into the kitchen and placed everything on the table.

"I went to Zatwarnica first," he said while he ate ravenously. "But nobody's there."

"Father died," I said. "My brother and sister were taken to work in Germany, and Mother took the younger children to live in Vienna."

"And my wife and children?" Uncle Leon asked. "Do you know anything about them?"

I could only shrug helplessly. "We went to your house after the Russians left but found it empty."

Uncle Leon's head drooped and his fist clenched.

"It seems that only you and I are left from all of the family," he said. "Such is the verdict of God." He wiped away some tears. "Here I'm crying like a woman and I have so many things to take care of. I must tell Mrs. Landow about her husband."

"What about her husband?"

"Come with me and you'll hear everything."

I laid out some clean clothes while Uncle Leon washed and shaved. After he had dressed and trimmed his hair we left together. In the kitchen of Mrs. Landow's house, Uncle Leon's face changed from smiling to grim.

"In October of 1939 I was arrested by the Russians and spent some time with your husband," he said to Mrs. Landow.

"Since his arrest I haven't heard of him," Mrs. Landow said. "Is he still alive?"

Uncle Leon shook his head sadly. "He died in my arms."

Mrs. Landow tried to contain her emotions. She reached out and clenched Uncle Leon's hand.

"Tell me everything," she said. "I have to know."

"The Russians kept us locked in a cellar not far from here," he said. "They beat us to extract confessions, of what we were not always sure. That's how I lost my eye."

"I'm sorry," Mrs. Landow said.

"They accused your husband of mistreating the poor," Uncle Leon went on. "When he denied it, they broke his fingers and tried to force him to sign a confession, but he refused."

"My husband is a stubborn and proud man," Mrs. Landow said. "And very charitable to the poor."

"We can all attest to that," I said.

"After nine days they told us that everybody who could walk would be taken to Russia where we would get work and food. We knew that whatever we were about to face would be better than staying there with the dead and dying. Mr. Landow had difficulty walking so I helped him out of the cellar and onto one of the trucks."

"My blessing on you," Mrs. Landow said.

"There were about a hundred of us, the stronger helping the weak. The sun nearly blinded us but the fresh air gave us strength and hope. They drove us to a train where other trucks were also arriving. Then the Russian soldiers herded us into cattle cars and locked the doors from the outside."

Uncle Leon watched Mrs. Landow's face for a signal that she had heard enough but she nodded for him to continue.

"It was cold on the train. We were loaded as tightly as sardines. The stink was horrible from our own waste and covered the floor. We slept on those dirty floors for five nights, on top of each other. We got no food or water. Many died from dehydration and starvation but most from exhaustion. They couldn't take any more."

Uncle Leon reached out and touched Mrs. Landow.

"I tried very hard to keep your husband alive," he said softly. "But life just escaped from him. He was the only friend I had on that condemned journey, and he left me. I was angry at him for doing it. It was as if he had escaped to a better life and left me behind to suffer some more. I cried for him and for myself, but my cries were not heard because all around me others were crying too."

Uncle Leon paused to collect himself.

"When morning came the train stopped and the guards opened the doors. They told us to throw out the dead. We did. I threw my friend, your husband, out of the train. When the cleanup was done they brought us water and soup. Then they locked the doors and the train started to move again, leaving the dead behind in a strange land.

Who buried them and whether their graves are marked, I don't know."

Mrs. Landow lowered her head and started to weep. Her lips moved in prayer, first in silence and then aloud as she prayed for the dead in Hebrew. Uncle Leon and I bowed our heads and prayed too.

"I'm sorry but I felt my husband's presence," Mrs. Landow said. "He was so close I could almost touch him. I said a prayer for him and, do you know, I feel better. Now tell us about yourself, dear friend. How did you manage to come home?"

"I was working in a mine in Ural when there was an explosion," Uncle Leon said. "Many prisoners were killed. I had burns on my legs and was taken to a hospital. One night I slipped outside and killed a guard with my bare hands. I had no pity. I remembered all the people they had killed without pity, and my hatred gave me the strength to choke him to death. I walked from village to village, through forests, eating only what I could steal, until I passed through the German lines and made it home to Poland."

"Now what will you do?" Mrs. Landow asked.

"Try and find my family," Uncle Leon said. "Failing that, I will join the Polish partisans and exact what revenge I can."

I stared at my uncle with new respect.

"God be with you," Mrs. Landow said.

The next morning, after breakfast, I packed some clean clothes for Uncle Leon and included some food and money.

"Where will you go first?" I asked.

"To my house on the River San," Uncle Leon said. "Maybe I can find some trace of my wife and children there. Then I'll go into the mountains." He touched my cheek. "Write your mother and tell her I'm alive and healthy, and someday we'll see each other again. But don't tell her I've joined the Polish underground. The Germans could make trouble for all of you."

He embraced me and left by the back door. I watched through the window as he disappeared down the road. I was still lost in gloomy thought when there was a knock on the front door. I opened it and to my astonishment saw Petrusia standing there. We shouted at the same time and fell into each other's arms.

"I'd like to come back and work for you," Petrusia said. "My mother died and there's not much left to do on the farm. This way I'll have a family again."

I was delighted.

"You can have your old room back," I said, "without the Russians! It'll be like old times."

Chapter Twenty-Six

A few weeks later Mr. Friedes hurried over to see Jan and me.

"Hoculak and the mayor had a meeting with the Jewish leaders," he said. "They told us that Jews will be allowed to work for Poles and Ukrainians but only for food, not money. Who needs money? All we need is food. So I can work for you and you can pay us with what you wish and we don't have to be secretive about it. What do you think of that change of heart?"

"I can't believe it," I said with wide-open eyes. "It must be a trick. We'll have to wait and see."

"Yes, we'll see," Mr. Friedes said. "Hoculak also said there's a plan for Jews to be sent away from here. He said the Germans have built camps and need people to work in them. Maybe they'll send us there and we'll get good food and a warm place to live. It'll be better than sitting here, waiting for a miracle, don't you think?"

"Maybe it'll be better," Jan said. "My brother Edward's in one of those camps but we haven't heard anything from him. So I can't tell you anything about them. But maybe it'll be better."

☒   ☒   ☒

The first week in June, Jan came home shaking his head.

"Hoculak's thugs have spread the word. Jews and Ukrainians in Lutowiska are allowed to practice a little black market unofficially. So people from other villages have filled up the marketplace with all kinds of food—butter, eggs, even the odd chicken. I don't get it."

"At least the Jews will be able to eat decently," I said.

Through the window I saw Mr. Friedes coming back from town and waved to him.

"What's going on?" I asked.

"It's certain Hoculak is trying to bilk us of our valuables," Mr. Friedes said cautiously when he came over. "This is one of his tricks to lure out our gold and American money. They won't accept Polish money from us. We know this, but how can we resist the food, trick or not? I took two pairs of new shoes to market and exchanged them for fifty kilos of flour and two chickens. Can you imagine? We don't have to be afraid to trade and our sick Jewish families will get healthy. And so I say who cares what Hoculak's motives are!"

☒   ☒   ☒

Janka Helder and her father showed up unexpectedly at my house. They looked unusually sullen.

"What a pleasant surprise," I said. "What brings you to Lutowiska?"

"The black market," Mr. Helder said grimly. "We've come to exchange food we don't need for goods we may soon need."

I was puzzled by the remark but invited them in.

"How's Zbyshek?" I asked. "Have you heard from him?"

"He was wounded on the Russian front," Janka said. "A bullet went through his chest, barely missing his heart."

"Oh my God! How is he now?"

"Still in the hospital but recovering nicely," Janka said.

"Good, I'll write to him," I said brightly.

"You can't," Janka said. "He's a German soldier."

"You can send a letter for me, can't you?"

Janka started to say something but looked at her father instead.

"Yes, we can send it for you," Mr. Helder said. "But I don't know if you'll get an answer. We're leaving Zatwarnica in the next few days and moving to Sanok. From there we'll be transported to Germany. The Germans are taking people of German origin and shipping them to the Fatherland. We have no choice, we have to go. But that's not the only reason we're moving. After what I saw in the woods, I don't want to stay here anymore."

"What did you see?" I asked.

"I'd rather not tell you, it'll scare you. You should leave these mountains too and join your mother in Vienna. You can still get a pass from the Germans but you have to act now. It's dangerous to stay here much longer."

"What did you see?" I pressed. "I promise you it won't scare me."

"You mustn't say I told you," Mr. Helder reluctantly said. "It would endanger my family."

I nodded my assent.

"I was hunting in the forest behind your grandfather's estate when I heard voices," Mr. Helder said. "Through the branches I could see Milich and his wife and children surrounded by Ukrainian police."

"I know the Miliches," I said. "They put our family up at their house when I was a little girl."

"Milich's hands were folded on his chest as if in prayer," Mr. Helder continued. "The children were crying and clinging to their mother. Just beyond them there was an open trench. I froze when I saw it. Suddenly one of the policemen grabbed Milich's boy, put a pistol to his head and shot him."

"Sweet Jesus!" I said with horror and disbelief. "I can't believe it!"

"Believe it," Mr. Helder said solemnly. "I saw it. Milich jumped at the man but two others grabbed him and a third smashed his face with a rifle butt. Mrs. Milich didn't move. She stared straight ahead without emotion, like she was already dead. They proceeded to shoot the other children and threw them into the trench. Then they shot Mr. and Mrs. Milich and rolled them into the trench too."

I started to cry.

"I can't believe it!" I said. "You had a hunting rifle. Why didn't you use it?"

Mr. Helder lowered his head and shook it sadly.

"I thought about it," he said, "but there were too many of them and I was terrified. They would have killed me and my family. We would have all ended up with the Miliches. I was a soldier in the first world war and saw men killed, but I've never seen children murdered." He looked at me. "There's a tremendous evil festering and growing in this land, Victoria. Beware of it."

I sat silently, terrifying thoughts going through my mind, thoughts of disbelief and anguish. Mr. Helder stood up and took my hand.

"If they are killing Jews now," he said, "they might decide to kill Poles too. That's why you should leave while there's still time."

Janka embraced me, said goodbye and went out with her father. I was left alone with grief in my heart. Grief and alarm. I knew I had to warn the Jews in Lutowiska, but whom should I tell? The Friedes? No, they would be terrified. I decided to run and tell Dr. Shline. He'd know what to do.

I hurried to Dr. Shline's office and waited until he was alone. Then I repeated the story. Dr. Shline was calm but in his eyes I could see great fear and concern. He was silent for a long time.

"Dr. Shline, please say something," I said. "You've got to warn the others. You've got to hide! Don't you believe me?"

"I believe every word," Dr. Shline said. "Helder's an honest man. But something puzzles me. If the Ukrainian police are killing Jews in secrecy, in small villages like Zatwarnica, it must be without the knowledge of the Germans. I don't think they would try that here where we have thousands of Jews. And I don't think they'd be stupid enough to kill us in front of Poles, or Ukrainians for that matter. Hoculak told us we're being shipped to German work camps because the Germans are fighting a big war and need us. I don't think the Ukrainians are brave enough to go against German orders."

"What you say makes sense," I said. "But I'm still very frightened for you and the others."

Dr. Shline patted my hand.

"I'll talk to the Jewish leaders tonight," he said. "We'll decide what to make of this. I won't tell them where I got the information."

I left Dr. Shline's office with some relief in my heart. I felt Dr. Shline was a very smart man and would know what to do.

An ashen-faced Zawacki came over and started speaking before he was even in the house.

"The entire Polanski family has been viciously massacred," he said. "Just eight kilometers from here, in the village of Stuposiany. I'm on my way there because I knew them."

"They were friends of my grandfather too," I said. "We'll go with you."

On the way, Zawacki told us how the Polish government had awarded land to Polanski's father.

"It was for bravery in the fight for our Free Polish Republic," he said. "Now we have Germans, Russians and Ukrainians spilling our blood to steal our land away."

When we arrived at the Polanski house there was a group of people milling around outside.

"Don't go in there," one of the neighbors said. "I wish I hadn't."

But we went in. There were men inside with horrified looks on their faces. I saw something bloody sticking out of the brick oven. I made a move to go closer but Jan stopped me. I could see that it was a young boy. His tongue and his eyes had been cut out. I gasped and covered my eyes.

In the bedroom Mrs. Polanski and her two children were lying in a pool of blood that was coagulated and black. They had been horribly disfigured. An unborn fetus had been savagely cut out of her. The daughter was lying nearby, a thick stake protruding from between her legs. The father was in the back yard, his penis cut off and his guts ripped out and replaced with manure.

My head started to reel. I opened my mouth to scream but nothing came out. I started to collapse but was caught by Jan and Zawacki who took me back to the carriage. We headed home in grim silence.

"Who could have committed such a heinous crime?" I finally asked.

"Only a satan from hell," Jan said. "No human could have done this to another human."

"It had to be the Ukrainians," Zawacki said.

"Why do you say that?" Jan asked.

"The stake in the little girl. Ukrainians have always said that was the way Poles killed Cossack women years ago. This is their revenge."

Days later, after coffins had been made from rough boards by the Polanskis' neighbors and friends, the long procession of horse-drawn wagons carried the mutilated bodies to the cemetery. No priest was there to say a prayer, only a little boy who ran to the church and tolled the bells.

After the wave of shock had blown over, I met again with Dr. Shline.

"They've killed Jews in Zatwarnica and Poles in Stuposiany," I said. "If we don't do something, they'll kill us all!"

"Victoria, you're such a child," Dr. Shline said irritably. "What can we do? We're helpless."

"We can escape!"

"Where? With women, children and old people, how far could we go? Besides, there is no safe place."

Chapter Twenty-Seven

O n June 6 in 1942, at dawn, strange and disturbing
noises were heard from the direction of the Roman
Catholic church. Sounds of hacking and the screech-
ing of shovels told of the toilsome breaking and digging of
ground.

The thick heavy fog lifted. Like drops of tears, the
morning dew covered the grass and meadows. The sun
rose, showering the earth with golden rays. Except for the
distant sound of digging, Lutowiska was unusually quiet.

Jan left for work at the regular time but returned within
a few minutes.

"The police stopped me and sent me home," he said.
"We're not supposed to be out on the street today."

"Why not?" I asked. "What's going on?"

"I don't know, but I saw so many police it gives me the
shivers. I wonder where the hell they came from and what
they're doing here. They must be having maneuvers of
some kind."

I went to the window and looked out. Small groups of people were going into the courthouse.

"Why is everybody going there?" I asked. "I can see families with children and babies."

Jan and Petrusia joined me at the window.

"They look like Jewish families," Petrusia said.

"She's right," I said. "There are the Friedes." I ran out onto the porch and waved my hand. "Mr. Friedes! Where are you going?"

Mr. Friedes started to say something but a policeman waved his rifle at me.

"Go back inside!" he shouted. "You're not allowed on the street!"

"I'm not on the street!" I snapped. "I want to know where they're going and why!"

The policeman came up to me.

"They're not going anywhere," he said. "Only into the courthouse to be registered, that's all. Nothing to get excited about."

"Thank God that's all," I said with relief. "I was afraid you were taking them to the work camps."

I watched the Friedes family join the procession of Jews. A cordon of police was watching them very closely. I went back into the house and found Mr. Zawacki talking to my husband.

"He came through the back fence," Jan said.

"Did you see all those policemen out there?" I asked. "Why do they need so many for only registration?"

"They're all going in but they're not coming out," Zawacki said. "That's a lot of people to keep cooped up in such a small building."

"What do you think is going on in there?" Jan asked.

"We'll have to wait and see," Zawacki said. "There's not much else we can do."

Jan took a bottle of vodka out of the cupboard and offered some to Zawacki but Zawacki declined.

"I'm going to see what I can find out," Zawacki said and slipped out the back door.

Jan poured some vodka into a large glass and emptied it in one swallow. I watched in disgust as he refilled the glass.

"Why do you always get drunk whenever there's a problem?"

"What problem?" Jan said. "I don't see a problem. For the Jews maybe, but not for us."

"I'm afraid of what's going to happen today," I said. "I have such a bad premonition. And all you can do is drink!"

"And what can you do?" he growled.

Jan took the bottle to the sofa where he stretched out and closed his eyes. After several more drinks he fell asleep.

I kept looking out the window and watching the courthouse. By noon, fewer and fewer people were going in. By late afternoon the streets were deserted except for the policemen who were patrolling the area. Soon darkness swept the earth. Stars covered the sky and a full moon discreetly reappeared from behind the clouds. I noticed that the police were doubling the watch around the courthouse.

"Something's happening," I said to Petrusia. "Maybe they're finally being released."

"I hear a strange noise," Petrusia said.

For one second there was complete silence. Then we heard the rumble of wagons. Six pulled up in front of the courthouse. Hoculak got down from one of them and went inside. The courthouse door opened and the Jews came staggering out, desperately gasping for fresh air. They grumbled and moaned but they stayed inside the wall of heavily armed police.

"Into the wagons!" I heard Hoculak shout. "Families stay together!"

People started to climb into the wagons in silence broken only by the groans of exhausted old men and the whimpering of frightened children. When all six wagons were loaded, they started to roll, escorted by some of the police.

"Where are they taking them?" I asked.

"God knows!" Petrusia said mournfully.

I looked over at Jan and listened to him snore. It made me more and more disgusted. Then I heard the sound of wagons again.

"Six more," I said as I watched them pull up in front of the courthouse.

"The same ones," Petrusia said. "I recognize the horses. That means they can't be taking them far."

"But where?" I asked.

This time the people did not come out of the courthouse willingly. They were pushed and beaten by the angry police. When anybody resisted climbing into a wagon his face was pummeled with a rifle. The Jews started to fight back, kicking the policemen whenever they could. The police became enraged and turned on the Jews, striking them randomly. People clambered into the wagons and fell on top of each other, their shrill screams filling the air.

I caught sight of the Friedes family as they came out. They were very orderly and offered no resistance. They started to climb into the wagon when Mrs. Friedes looked at my house and waved. I couldn't take it any longer. I opened the door and ran out onto the street.

"Mrs. Friedes!" I called out and ran to the wagon. "I love you and I'll remember you forever!"

Through the screams Mrs. Friedes heard my cry.

"They are taking us to our death!" she shouted to me. "We will all die, but you must tell the world what happened here tonight!"

One of the policemen hit Mrs. Friedes in the face with his rifle butt and she fell into the wagon. Another came up to me and swung at my head but I deflected the blow with my hands and ran back to the house. Petrusia opened the door to let me in and then quickly slammed it shut.

"You could have gotten killed!" she said.

I ran to the window. Tears rolled down my cheeks as I watched the wagons pull away.

"They're gone," I said. "But where?"

I started for the back door but stopped in front of Jan who was still snoring. I kicked him sharply in the leg and continued on into the back yard. I stood and listened. I could hear the muffled sound of voices in the distance. Petrusia came out and listened too.

"It's them," Petrusia said. "Not too far from here."

I shushed her. "It sounds like something's happening."

Suddenly, indistinct cries reached our ears followed by a series of shots. I crossed the back yard and listened some more. Now I heard screams. I continued on to Zawacki's house.

"Who's there?" Zawacki asked as he stepped out of the shadows.

"Can you hear that?" I asked.

"Yes. Shots coming from the church."

"I'm worried about the Jews," I said. "Maybe they're killing them."

"That can't be," Zawacki said. "They told me they were holding them in the courthouse because they were being shipped out today."

Now the shooting was rapid.

"Mr. Zawacki, listen to those shots! I'm telling you, they're killing the Jews! Just like they killed the Jews in Zatwarnica!"

I moved past him and headed for the street.

"Where are you going?" Zawacki called out. "Don't be foolish."

"To the church," I said. "I have to find out what's going on."

I could see police patrolling the deserted street so I crept into the deep ditch and followed it. I felt protected by an unfolding blanket of mist. As I got closer, the sounds of gunfire and screaming grew louder. I came to the footbridge in front of the church and peeked through the tall weeds.

In the dim light I could see a freshly dug pit to the left of the church. Policemen with rifles were watching a ragged line of people coming out of the barn behind the church. Many were crying and trying to resist, but the police kicked them and prodded them along with their bayonets. Some tried to fight back but they were immediately pounced on and beaten senseless.

I held my breath as the people were lined up at the pit. Hoculak stepped forward and made a motion with his hand. Shots were fired and people fell backward into the dark hole to disappear from sight. One of the policeman moved up to the edge of the pit and fired a burst of shots into it.

"One bullet for each Jew!" Hoculak said.

"But they're not all dead!" the policeman said.

"They will be soon enough," Hoculak said. "Bring out the rest."

My head spun and I fell to the bottom of the ditch. I felt a man's hand on my mouth and tried to wriggle free. I twisted my head around and saw that it was Zawacki.

"We have to get out of here before they see us!" he whispered in my ear. "Or we'll be shot too!"

He took my hand and led me away. Behind us the executions continued.

When I got back to the house I went into the bedroom and fell on the bed. The resonance of the shooting reached my ears even though I tried to cover them. Each shot went through my heart like a knife.

"Sweet Jesus!" I cried. "Each shot takes a life! When will they stop?"

I started to pray for the dying innocent.

"Cry with me, oh my God, for my eyes are dry. I can cry no more. My soul is empty. My heart is torn. The blood of your children cries to Heaven for vengeance. Cry with me, oh my God!"

As daybreak came my eyes turned to the window. The heavy mist had lifted. Birds awakened, chirping the most beautiful melodies. The sun showed a streak of gold from beyond the horizon. A cool breeze swayed the tall grass and rustled the leaves on trees. I sat up and listened. Except for the birds and the breeze, all was silence. It was over.

"They killed them all," I said quietly. "All the Jews are dead."

Bitterness clouded my heart. Bitterness at people, at God, at the whole world. I went into the parlor and looked down at Jan, still asleep on the couch.

"Get up," I said and nudged him. "Something horrible has happened."

But Jan didn't wake up. He mumbled something, turned over and continued to snore. I was about to wake him forcibly when I heard the back door open. I went into the kitchen and saw one of the Friedes girls standing by the door. Her hair was tangled with weeds and dirt. Her face was scratched and her clothes covered with blood stains. Her beautiful blue eyes were red from crying. She was shaking from fright.

I rushed over to her and touched her face.

"Lika," I said softly. "Come and sit down."

Lika took a few steps, then staggered. I helped her to the chair.

"How did you get here?" I asked. "How did you escape?"

Lika responded weakly, "I'm so tired, and so thirsty."

I filled a glass with water and handed it to her. She put it to her lips with shaking hands and drank it down. I moistened a towel and wiped her face. Petrusia came into the kitchen and gasped when she saw Lika but I motioned her to be quiet.

"I'm very sleepy," Lika said and stood up. "I have to go. I don't want them to hurt you and your family."

I stopped her.

"You can't go out there. You'll have to hide in our cellar. We'll bring you some food and blankets and you can sleep down there."

⬛　⬛　⬛

The church bells rang for morning prayer. The sad tolling permeated the town with mourning. People started to come out of their homes. I joined them as we walked to church in small groups. We moved silently past the huge mound of fresh dirt. No one said a word but we all knew what had happened in the night.

Inside the church, instead of singing the morning hymn, we said the litany for the dead. The bells kept ringing slowly, as for a funeral. When the litany was finished we left the church one by one and stopped by the mound to make the sign of the cross. Somebody whispered that it was ground blessed by the bishop when the church was built.

"My blessing on you and on your house," I remembered Mr. Friedes saying.

When Jan finally woke up I told him what had happened the night before. He was horrified.

"I suspected this all along," he said. "I think we'll be next. That worries me."

"Don't say that, you're frightening me!" I shouted. "And if you're so worried, why did you get so drunk?"

"I had to. That way I don't have to hear or see anything."

"You're a coward," I said.

Jan paid no attention to me. He finished dressing and left for work. I was glad I hadn't told him about Lika. I wasn't sure I could trust him. I felt confident about Zawacki, however, and went over to see him.

"You look frightened and nervous," Zawacki said.

"I am, but not for me," I said. "For Lika Friedes."

"Lika?" Zawacki asked with surprise.

"She's in my house, in the cellar. And I don't know what to do with her."

Zawacki nodded in sympathy. "When the town settles down we'll have to get them both out of here to someplace safe."

"Both?" Now it was my turn to act surprised.

"Erlich's eldest son is hiding in my loft," Zawacki said. "He was able to crawl through some loose boards in the barn and get away."

"Praise God for at least that much," I said. "Where will you take them? To Sheila Landow's hiding place in the forest?"

Zawacki stared at me without replying, as if a trust had been broken.

"I know it exists," I went on. "I just don't know where."

"I can't take them there," Zawacki said. "The woods are crawling with Banderovtsi, Bandera's guerrilla army."

"Then where will you take them?"

"When the time comes, I will tell you."

A few days later Zawacki asked me to have Lika and Erlich dressed in Ukrainian clothes. He wanted them ready to go by five in the morning. I did as I was asked and sat nervously by the window watching the dark skies and listening to the rain tapping on the window panes. What was going to happen to those two young people, I wondered. Would they be able to escape the messengers of Satan pursuing them?

When Zawacki's horse-drawn wagon was ready he gave a signal and Lika and Erlich came out of the barn. I could barely see them. They were concealed by the dark and rainy morning. They climbed into the back of the wagon, crawled under a canvas and, with a rumble of wheels, were gone. I let out a deep breath.

"God help them on their journey," I said. "Please God, lead them to safety."

Days passed before Zawacki came back.

"Now will you tell me where you took them?" I asked eagerly.

"To a remote valley near the Russian border," Zawacki said. "We ran into Jews in flight from Krakow. I knew that many of them were from Sheila Landow's group but they admitted nothing. They were on their way to Palestine."

"By way of Russia?"

"Is there another way?" Zawacki asked grimly. "There were hundreds of them so I thought it was safe to let Lika and Erlich go with them. May God help them to a safe place."

"Thank God!" I said. "Maybe God will be good to us now and sweep all this misfortune away."

Chapter Twenty-Eight

*I*n the summer of 1942, horrifying news reached Lutowiska. It came with a young man galloping through town on horseback.

"Murder!" he shouted. "Orphans in Lomna murdered! Priest and nuns murdered!"

A policeman tried to stop him but the young man turned his horse around and galloped away. The policeman fired a shot after him but he was already out of range.

A large number of townspeople drove or ran the short distance to Lomna. Jan and I went too. Lomna was a small village in the mountains, and the people who lived there were all farmers. There was a church with one priest, five nuns and about forty orphans. They had survived the Russian occupation because the villagers had hidden them in their homes.

"I was delivering food to the nuns," a farmer said as we gathered around. "I saw the door wide open and went inside. There were dead bodies everywhere. One of the nuns was still alive and told me a group of armed men who pretended to be police slaughtered them all. I sent that messenger to warn you, and another to inform the German police."

Hoculak and some of his men showed up and started to take charge.

"Go home!" Hoculak shouted at the crowd. "There's nothing for you to do here!"

"We're waiting for the German police!" the farmer said.

Soon a small truck arrived with five German policemen. They went into the convent and came out quickly.

"We'll investigate these murders," the officer said. "The killers will be punished."

They climbed back into their truck and drove away.

"You heard what the man said," Hoculak growled. "The killers will be punished."

Then he and his men left too.

Terrified, we went back to Lutowiska and armed ourselves with pitchforks, hatchets, scythes and knives. At my request, Jan put shutters on the windows that could be bolted from the inside. The next day two German policemen arrived in Lutowiska and set up their headquarters in the rectory. Mayor Kochut and his pretty young maid had to move into one of the empty Jewish homes. He was unhappy at this indignity and let everybody know.

Perhaps because of the presence of the German police, everything remained quiet throughout the rest of the summer. The potatoes were harvested and Zawacki was able to smuggle seven wagon loads of them into the forest for Sheila Landow and her people. But then, on a cold fall day, the bodies of a war widow and her seven children were found in their home. Their throats had been slashed and their bodies mutilated.

"Why would anybody want to kill those poor people?" I asked upon hearing the news. "There was nothing to take from them. They knew nothing of politics. They weren't even living. They barely existed on the potatoes they helped us harvest."

"Don't be naive," Jan said. "They were killed because they're Poles. Soon we'll all be killed, and I think I know who's doing it."

"Then report it to the police," I said.

"Which police? Hoculak already knows, and the German police don't give a damn. They didn't even go to the scene of the crime. I think we're all condemned people here."

I felt sick to my stomach, and it wasn't only because I was pregnant again. I knew I would soon be bringing a third child into a world that seemed to be controlled by the devil.

Chapter Twenty-Nine

March, 1943. I was expecting my baby any day and feeling surprisingly good despite the way things were, and despite the shortage of medicine and food.

"That's because you're a natural mother," Petrusia said.

"If only the times were better for it," I said.

Jan walked in from work followed by Mr. Zawacki. They both looked distressed.

"What's going on?" I asked.

"Last night all the people in the village of Polana were murdered," Zawacki said.

"All?" I asked, my voice trembling.

Zawacki nodded soberly.

"The evil strikes again," Jan snarled. "They won't stop until they spill the last drop of Polish blood. May they rot in hell!"

"The Germans are mad as hell too," Zawacki said. "Those farmers were good producers of grain and cattle."

"That's all the Germans care about!" Petrusia said.

"They also want the people of Lutowiska to bury the dead."

"How generous of them," Jan said.

"It's the least we can do," I said.

About fifty townspeople assembled in the square, mostly men and a few women. Mrs. Zawacki and I came too. We set out on foot to Polana. Hoculak and a German policeman followed on horseback. The sad procession stopped on a hill overlooking Polana. We could see no sign of life in the village. We walked down into the valley and came to the first house. Zawacki and some men went in. Zawacki came out with an infant.

"The family's all dead but this baby's alive," he said and gave the child to his wife.

People dispersed through the village to check every house for more survivors. Meanwhile, some of the men started to dig trenches near the victims' homes. Others went to the barns and let the hungry cattle out. When the trenches were deep enough the men started carrying bodies out of the houses and laying them side by side in the trenches. A man came out of a house with a frightened little girl and brought her to Mrs. Zawacki and me.

"I found her behind the fireplace," he said. "She won't speak. She only stares."

"We'll take care of her," I said. I put my arm around the little child and drew her close.

Another man brought a small boy out of the cabbage field. The boy was shaking. His eyes were wide open in terrified fright. I stroked his head.

"Don't be afraid," I said. "We're here to help you."

The German policeman saw the children and came over.

"You can take them home and feed them," he said. "But I'll have to ask headquarters what they want to do with them."

Mrs. Zawacki and I gathered up the children and started for home. The boy kept looking back at his village as the burial continued. I turned to look too. No funeral procession and no coffins, I remember thinking. No church bells and no priests or prayer. No laments and no cries of relatives. No one left to mourn. They had all died together on the same night. God had opened the heavens and taken them to his kingdom for eternal peace. Their immortal souls were at rest with the saints and the angels.

The following day on March 18, the German police came and picked up the orphaned children. That was the same day I gave birth to my third son. We called him Adam.

Chapter Thirty

In April of 1944 I was in the back yard when I saw Mr. Zawacki motion to me. I met him at the rear of his house.

"They're holding a Jew at the police station," he said in a husky whisper. "They found him in the Carynskie forest and suspect he's from Sheila Landow's group. If he talks, I'm a dead man. My family and I are leaving as soon as possible. You can come with us."

"I can't," I said. "I love a man in the Banderovtsi. He said he would watch over me. I'm going to wait for him until he comes."

Zawacki stared at me with great astonishment.

"This is unbelievable," he said, "but I think I understand. Goodbye, my young friend. Maybe fate will bring us together again."

At dawn the next morning I heard a commotion and looked out the window. I saw the police climbing into their wagons. They were all heavily armed. Hoculak and Mayor Kochut were sitting in the first wagon along with the Jew, bound and gagged and squatting at their feet. Hoculak gave the signal and the caravan rolled out of town.

I spent an anxious day waiting for them to come back. I was certain the Zawackis were already gone so I had nowhere to get information. I remained in the garden planting vegetables until I saw the caravan coming back to the courthouse. Then I went into the house and watched from behind a curtain.

Hoculak jumped down from the wagon first and shouted orders. His men started to carry what looked like wounded and dead policemen into the courthouse. Obviously something terrible had happened in the forest. I wondered whether Sheila and her people got away. I hoped to God that they did.

There was dread in my heart as I went back to my garden and continued to plant vegetables. I bent low to the ground, afraid to lift my head and look at the courthouse. Behind me the sun set, a red crescent on the horizon. Red as if the sun had absorbed the blood that was spilled in the forest.

The next day there was a big funeral at the Ukrainian church for the police who were killed in action against the Jewish Resistance. They lost fourteen, I heard someone say, but they wiped out at least three hundred Jews on Carynskie mountain. My heart sank.

Hoculak was furious that Zawacki had escaped from under his nose. Every Pole was immediately brought in for interrogation. Jan was questioned too and came home with a bloody nose and bruises all over his body.

"Curse the Ukrainians!" he shouted at Petrusia and me. "Curse the Germans, and curse Zawacki too!"

Instead of cursing, I took the children to church where I prayed for relief from this terror. But when I saw that the two German policemen were gone and their office closed, I had an awful feeling that my prayers had not been heard. The terror was probably just beginning.

Boom!

A muffled roar from far away reached our ears in the town square. We lifted our heads and listened urgently.

"Did you hear that?" a woman asked.

"I think it's thunder," a man said. "We may get a storm tonight."

I looked up. The sky was clear with only a few clouds.

"That was not thunder," an old man said. "The Russian front is coming closer. We may soon have Russians in our town again."

The children and I had just turned for home when Jan came galloping past on horseback.

"Where are you going?" I called out to him.

"Goodbye, Victoria!" he called back. "Goodbye children!"

He spurred the horse and galloped away.

Evening came and Jan didn't show up. Petrusia put the children to bed while I locked the doors and bolted the shutters. I fell asleep thinking I would hear Jan come in. But he didn't come home that night and he wasn't there in the morning.

"Where could he have gone?" Petrusia asked.

"I'm sure he left to save his skin," I said. "He doesn't give a damn about me or the children."

Petrusia went home for a few days to tend to a parcel of potatoes, and I assumed all household chores. This way I had less time to think about Ivan and what he might be doing. Three Polish families in the village of Ruskie had just been murdered and their homes burned. And in Stuposiany, the last few farmers had been slaughtered. I wondered whether Ivan knew about them. And did he know about the farmers who came to Lutowiska to seek refuge from the Banderovtsi? They felt safer here where there were police—Ukrainian police but still police.

That evening I put the children to bed as usual but instead of locking the house up I went outside and sat on the porch. The night was unusually quiet. Even the courthouse was quiet. The aroma of blooming jasmine drifted by on the evening breeze. Suddenly my heart started to pound as an indescribable fear seized me. I started to shake as if with fever.

What's happening to me? I wondered. Why am I so scared?

I went inside and quickly locked the doors and bolted the shutters. I lay on the bed with my clothes on and my eyes wide open, listening and waiting, I didn't know for what. I crossed myself and started to pray. I heard muffled screams and sat up. I heard more screams only now they were more distinct. I was petrified.

"My God! The Banderovtsi are coming to kill us!"

I snatched the sleeping children from their beds and carried them down into the cellar one by one. I was tucking them into a makeshift bed when I heard footsteps near the house. I ran back upstairs in time to hear the sound of breaking glass. It was followed by the noise of shutters being broken open. I looked at the window and saw two men climbing through it. They were wearing silver badges with a trident insignia and the letters U.P.A.

"Where's your husband?" one of them asked.

"He took the children and abandoned me!" I said quickly.

Rough hands grabbed me and pushed me out the window. I didn't scream so as not to alarm the children. I was dragged through the yard and into the street where other people were scuffling with armed men. Squeals of children and cries of women penetrated the quiet night and echoed through the mountains.

My eyes were wide with terror. God save my babies! I kept repeating in my mind. God, don't let them find my children!

We were quickly surrounded by men with silver badges. Some of us tried to fight back and a bloody scuffle broke out. Hoculak's police joined in and helped beat the protesters into submission. I watched paralyzed with fear as heads were split open and chests were pierced by bayonets. My screams stuck in my throat. I couldn't make a sound.

I lifted my eyes to the armed man standing next to me. He said something like "Move!" or "Go!" But my eyes were fixed on the silver badge he was wearing. Its trident and letters shined in the moonlight. U.P.A., the Ukrainian Insurgent Army. Banderovtsi. Ivan Fedorchyk's group. My Ivan! He sent them to kill us like they killed the Jews!

We were pushed and dragged towards the church where we were joined by hundreds of others. The bodies of those who had resisted lined the road. Our screams turned into a roar. When we came to the church the doors were thrown wide open and we were herded inside. The Banderovtsi followed, weapons held high, and the gruesome slaughter began.

People fell to their knees and shouted prayers as gunfire echoed through the church and bullets cut them down like wheat falling to a scythe. I stood trembling, my eyes closed tightly, and waited for a bullet to find me.

"Ivan, where are you?" I shouted into the deafening roar. "Why don't you come and save me?"

A sharp object hit me in the chest. I fell between the pews. I felt a burning pain, and then peace.

The sun rose. The screaming inside the church had ceased. Some of the victims were still moaning but life was escaping them like a candle flickering out. I could smell the stench of gunpowder, blood and human excrement. As if in a dream, I heard the sound of a door being unbolted and swinging open. Daylight brightened the inside of the church. Footsteps came closer, and then voices.

"Major Melnik," I heard a man ask. "Why are you avoiding walking on Polish blood?"

"I don't want to dirty my boots," was the reply. The voice was Ivan's.

Ivan! At last he had come to save me! But too late! Too late!

"We are the Ukrainian Insurgent Army," Ivan said as his footsteps came closer. "Some army, slaughtering women and babies. There are more of them here than men. Are we supposed to be proud that we killed them?"

"Yes!" the man said. "They were sacrificed for our Ukrainian homeland."

I let out a moan.

"Someone's alive here!" Ivan said.

I felt movement and then saw Ivan's face staring down at me.

"Victoria!" he gasped in horror. "My God, what have I done!"

He lifted me up off the floor and put me on the pew.

"Victoria!" he whispered and touched my face. "It's me, Ivan. I warned you to go! Why didn't you go?"

He bent over me and kissed me on the mouth.

"Ivan!" I was able to say and closed my eyes again.

"No, don't die!" Ivan said. "Live for me, for us!"

"Major Melnik, what's going on?" the man asked suspiciously. "You know we can't have any witnesses."

"I know," Ivan said. "She's an old sweetheart. But I know my duty."

I opened my eyes and stared into the barrel of a pistol Ivan was holding. I looked at Ivan with love and pain. He smiled sadly.

"I will love you to the last breath in my body," he said. "But I have to do something against my will. Darling, close your eyes. I don't want you to suffer."

"I know what you have to do," I whispered. "But please save my children. They're hidden in the cellar, alone. My husband abandoned us." I closed my eyes. "I love you, Ivan."

I heard the deafening shot. I thought I was dead. Through the ringing in my ears I heard a body fall. A moment later I felt a soft touch on my face. I opened my eyes and looked into Ivan's sweet loving face. The body of his comrade lay crumpled at my side.

"It's all right," Ivan said. "I'll take care of you."

He kissed me gently and lifted me in his arms. He carried me to the altar and put me in the small space behind it. He tore open my blouse and applied a bandage to the wound that ran from my shoulder to below my breast.

"A nasty wound," he said, "but not very deep. You'll live, my sweet, and therefore so will I." He kissed me again. "Goodbye."

He walked away. The door slammed shut and the bolt locked.

▨   ▨   ▨

I could hear the marauding begin. While my dead neighbors lay inside the church in awful silence, their homes were being ransacked and then set ablaze. Flames leaped into the sky and lit up the dark night like fires of hell. I wanted to be dead too. It was then I felt somebody drag me out from behind the altar. A man's head pressed against my chest.

"She's still alive," the man said quietly. "Hurry!"

I felt myself being lifted and carried outside where I was placed in the back of a wagon and covered with straw. The wagon started to move. In the distance I could hear the yelling of unruly mobs. Through the straw I saw the terrible red glow of homes being consumed by fire.

My mind swirled. I had no idea what was happening. I remembered Ivan and my children and the gun being fired, and then I fell into that deep darkness that must have meant

I was dying. When I opened my eyes again it was daylight and Petrusia was smiling down at me.

"Petrusia," I said hoarsely. "I'm dead. What are you doing here?"

"You're not dead," Petrusia said. "You're alive and in my house."

"My children—!"

"They're here too," Petrusia said. "Brought by my cousin who was sleeping with one of the Banderovtsi. She was also the one who brought you here. I guess there's some good in all of us."

"I don't understand," I said.

"She said they were acting on Major Melnik's orders. You know him as Ivan Fedorchyk."

My lips quivered. "Oh Petrusia, the man that I love with all my heart is a killer!"

"He saved your life, and the lives of your children, didn't he? And at great risk to his own. He must be a fine man."

"But he's with the U.P.A., the Banderovtsi! I saw their badges! They slaughtered all the Poles in Lutowiska! I'd rather be dead than know he's one of them!"

Petrusia stroked my head with compassion.

"Maybe he had no choice," she said. "Maybe he has to belong to the U.P.A. because he's a Ukrainian."

"Ukrainians are evil!" I snapped. "I don't care if he saved my life!"

Petrusia lowered her head.

"I'm Ukrainian," she said quietly. "And may God forgive us for the crimes our people committed against all those poor souls."

"I didn't mean you," I said. "Petrusia, I loved him so. What am I going to do?"

"Right now you're going to rest. And then you're going to see the children. They've been asking for you."

Chapter Thirty-One

A month passed. I sat quietly in the corner of the attic where I had lain throughout my recovery. I thought about my life, the short happy life I had shared with Ivan. The rest was only a nightmare. The wounds on my body were healing but those in my heart and mind stayed open.

"I'll never forgive Ivan," I said when Petrusia came upstairs. "If somebody asked you to join the Banderovtsi and kill people, would you do it?"

"I could never kill a human being," Petrusia said and crossed herself fearfully.

"Ivan shouldn't have done it either," I said. "But he did."

"I found somebody who can take you to the trains that go west," Petrusia said. "Are you strong enough?"

"Yes, but how am I going to travel? I have no papers."

"We'll find a way. But you shouldn't stay here any longer. The Russian army's getting close. We can hear the constant roar of cannon, and the Banderovtsi are preparing to fight them."

"First the Jews, then the Poles, and now the Russians," I said with sarcasm. "Soon there will be no one left to murder except me and my children."

"We should leave tomorrow at dawn," Petrusia said.

"Are you coming with us?" I asked.

"Of course. Do you think I'd let you go with a strange man by yourself? Never! We're going together."

The trip through the rugged mountain forest was fearsome. We were fighting thick brush and walking stealthily so as not to encounter Banderovtsi, and that added to the time. Mitchel walked ahead with the guide. Val held my hand tightly and was not allowed to cry. Adam was being carried on Petrusia's back. At times even the guide carried him. At night we rested, and at dawn we made it the rest of the way to the railroad. I could see a crowd of young men and women being herded to the depot by German soldiers.

"Join this group when they come by," Petrusia said. "It looks like they're being sent to work in Germany."

I was stricken with fear. "Aren't you coming with us?"

"I can't," Petrusia said. "I have to return to my home."

Petrusia kissed the children and me and pushed us away as the crowd of young people came by. We were swept along. We stumbled up the ramp to the cattle cars and were pushed inside one of them. I looked back at Petrusia. She was still standing there, wiping her eyes with her apron. The door was closed and locked. I squatted on the floor, held my children close and started to cry. Little Mitchel put his arms around my neck.

"Don't cry, Mommy," he said. "When you cry I get scared."

I embraced my son and kissed him.

"Oh my little darling," I said. "Mommy will stop crying. Don't be afraid. I promise you Mommy will never cry again."

The train whistle blew. The car jerked and started to move. A young woman started to sing to a melody flowing from a harmonica. It was a song known to every Pole.

Rocked by the movement of the cattle car, Val and Adam soon fell asleep in my arms while Mitchel curled up at my side. I looked around at the strange faces beside me.

"Where are we going?" I asked the young woman sitting next to me.

"To Germany, where else?" she said. "How come you're here with your kids? They usually don't let them come with their mothers."

"We escaped from the Banderovtsi," I said.

The people around me raised their heads and listened quietly as I told them, between sobs, what was going on in the Carpathian Mountains. After a while, the train slowed and stopped and every ear turned to listen for what was going to happen next. The roar of an explosion rocked the train.

"We're being bombed!" somebody shouted.

"Good!" a man said. "Maybe we won't have to go any farther. We're still on Polish soil."

"I'd rather go to Germany and live," a woman said, "than stay here and die."

There was another boom and another, and then silence. The train started to move. It was a long time before we felt it stop again. A young man peered out through the slats.

"We're in Oswiecim," he said. "The Germans call it Auschwitz."

Everybody scrambled to look out.

"There's a concentration camp near here," a man said. "I've heard stories but nobody really knows what goes on there."

"That's where they send the Jews," a woman said.

Footsteps outside caught everybody's attention.

"Hide the kids," the young woman said, "or they'll take them away."

The women beside me wrapped their skirts around the children just as the door was opened by a German soldier. Two prisoners came up with a large kettle. Each person received a can of soup and a slice of dark bread. I shared mine with the children. In a few minutes the soldier called for the cans and the prisoners counted them as they were returned. The door was closed and locked and the train started to move. There was an audible sigh of relief.

When the train stopped once again, the unloading began.

"Line up! Line up!" a German soldier shouted

I held the children close and got in line.

"Please God, don't let them take my babies away," I prayed as the line moved forward to where the registration was in process. My body shook with fear when I faced a woman in a German uniform.

"Whose children are these?" the woman asked.

I staggered but suddenly my motherly strength came back. I would fight for my children. They would have to kill me before I would part with them.

"They're mine," I said firmly and looked directly into her eyes.

"We don't need women with children."

"Well, you have one. I didn't volunteer for this trip, you know."

"Step aside," the woman said.

"No I won't!" I said. "I can work as hard as anybody!"

The woman didn't answer immediately.

"Follow the line for delousing," she finally said.

Stripped naked and sprayed with powder, we were given ash-colored uniforms with a big P on them. I put mine on and then dressed the boys. I rolled up their sleeves and pant legs but they still looked like mushrooms under a tent, which stirred laughter among the others. One of the men picked up Adam and carried him on his shoulder.

"You're going to be our mascot," he said.

We were marched to a different building where there was food. We all pounced with ferocity on the potato and red-cabbage soup, dark bread, black coffee and water. We had hardly finished when the order came to get back on the train. As soon as everybody had scrambled back on board, the doors were closed and locked, the whistle blew and the train started to roll.

"We're entering Germany," somebody said.

"That's why we were deloused," somebody else said. "To keep the Fatherland pure."

Everybody laughed although uneasily.

Through the entire seven-hour ride there wasn't much talking. People were engrossed in their own thoughts and fears. We felt the train stop yet again. The doors opened on a dark and rainy night.

"Get out! Get out!" voices shouted in German from the ramp below.

A few men jumped down and helped the women.

"Hurry! Line up and march!"

We formed a line with guards on each side and began to march. When we reached a camp we stopped. Beyond the camp we could see a city.

"Kassel," somebody whispered.

"Shut up!" the guard said. "Women to the left! Men to the right!"

We had just separated into two groups when the air-raid sirens started to blow. We could hear the thunder of planes in the distance.

"Hit the ground!" the guard yelled.

I grabbed the children and crouched low. In a minute's time the bomber's flew overhead and explosions shook the earth. In the midst of huge fireballs and smoke, I saw two tall buildings in the city tumble down as if they were made of match sticks. The ground around us continued to shake for at least two more hours before the sirens sounded the all-clear.

We were finally marched to a long row of barracks. The children and I were sent into the first building. We were greeted by somber faces that just stared at us. One of the women got up from her bed and came over.

"My name is Zosia and that will be your bed," she said and pointed to an empty bunk in the corner. "We have many women here with children like yourself."

"Thank God for that," I said. "My name is Victoria. Is it very bad here?"

"Bad?" one of the other women said. "I've been here for two years and I can tell you it's never been this good."

"The Germans are losing the war," Zosia said. "So they're a little kinder to us."

I removed my wet clothes and the children's, and then all four of us slipped under a coarse blanket. The lights went off and we slept peacefully for the first time in many days.

In the morning, when the women were filing out for work, Zosia led me and the children across the yard to a large low building.

"They call this place the *Kindergarten*," she said. "That's German for children's garden. Some garden, eh? But it's not too bad. Women leave their kids here during the day."

She opened the door for me. I kissed the children and sent them inside with some misgivings.

"Don't worry," Zosia said. "The kids get fed, and at night they can be with you, which is much better than any other place. Believe me, I know."

I relaxed a bit. "Where do we go to work?"

Zosia pointed down at the ground.

"Under this mountain we're standing on," she said. "There's a five-story building beneath us. It's the largest factory in Germany. People work down there by the thousands."

I followed Zosia into a building hidden amongst the trees. I registered and got a pass. A large door opened in front of us and we entered a long corridor where other people were waiting. Soon a small train arrived and everybody got on board.

The ride was fast through a dark tunnel that felt like it was going downhill. I saw bright lights ahead and the tunnel opened into a huge hall filled with machines. We disembarked and Zosia waved and walked off. A German guard motioned for me to follow and led me to a big machine.

"This is where you'll work," he said. "Someone will be here to teach you. The rules are simple. No talking, no stealing, no sabotage. For that, the penalty is death. Understand?"

Afraid to speak, I just nodded my head.

The guard left and precisely at seven the machines started to roar. I stood by mine, bewildered. Eventually a man came up and said something in a language I didn't recognize. Through hand signals he was able to teach me how to operate the machine and before long I was making precision ball bearings. There was no room for error and I was careful of that. What the bearings were for I didn't know. Whatever the factory was producing was top secret.

■ ■ ■

One evening when I was standing in line to leave the factory, I saw a familiar face going the other way. Dear God, I realized, it was Jan! I started to say something when he happened to look at me.

"Victoria!" he shouted. "Is it really you?"

"Are you surprised," I said without emotion. "Especially since you left us to die?"

I continued to follow the line into the train.

"No, wait!" he said and ran after me. "Tell me the number of your barracks!"

He was still shouting as the door closed and the train pulled away.

Every fourteen days we were allowed a day off. I was sitting in the barracks with the children when the door opened and Jan came in.

"Mommy, it's Daddy!" Mitchel shouted.

The children ran up to him but I didn't move.

"So you found us," I said. "How nice."

Jan made a move to kiss me but I drew back.

"Still hurt because I left you, eh?"

"Not hurt, disgusted," I said. "You didn't care what happened to your own children."

"You don't understand," Jan said. "I got a threatening note telling me to leave. The Banderovtsi must have had it in for me because I was a friend of Zawacki's."

"What note?" I asked.

"A note warning me to leave before it was too late. Inside there was a little white daisy, a sure sign of death."

"A daisy?" I said.

My head spun. The note wasn't a threat against Jan at all. It was a message from Ivan warning me. I sat back on the bed and let my mind drift to Zatwarnica and the daisies in my grandfather's meadow.

Jan sat down beside me.

"Now that I've found you, we can live together," he said. "They have special barracks for families."

I came out of my reverie. "What if I told you that I don't want to live with you?"

Jan laughed but his face darkened. "You really don't mean that."

"Yes I do. I don't love you and I don't want to be with you."

He suddenly slapped me hard. When I tried to shield my face with my arms he struck me again and again. The children started to bawl.

"Stop hitting me!" I cried. "I'll come live with you, only stop hitting me!"

Jan's rage subsided as suddenly as it had ignited.

"Good girl," he said breathlessly. "Honey, I'm sorry. I love you and can't live without you, you know that. Why do you always make me so angry that I lose control?"

I just stared at him.

Next day, the children and I moved out of our barracks and into ones that were set aside for families. As I feared, Jan demanded his husband's rights. Also as I feared, I became pregnant.

"You said you'd be careful," I said to Jan. "What do we do now?"

"Nothing!" Jan barked. "Just don't tell anybody or we could be in big trouble."

"But how long can I hide it?"

"Don't worry, you're skinny," Jan said and walked away from me. "You won't show for a long time."

"And I wish you were dead," I muttered under my breath.

Chapter Thirty-Two

By September of 1944, the city of Kassel had been leveled by constant bombing. But the American planes continued to come by day, and the British by night.

"I wonder why they're wasting bombs on a city that's already been flattened," Zosia said on the way to work. "They must think there's something else around here."

Later, when I was oiling and cleaning my machine, a young man came up to me.

"Some rags for you," he said in German. "I have too many."

I looked down at the rags he was holding and saw that one of them was neatly folded.

"Hide that one on your body and smuggle it out of here," the young man said, now in fluent Polish. "It's a matter of life and death."

Shivers went down my spine but I nodded and tucked the folded rag inside my trousers.

"Thank you," the young man said. "You'll help end the war that much sooner."

When my shift ended, I grew nervous as I approached the checkpoint. I knew that if the guards searched us as occasionally they did, I'd be shot.

"Do you have any parts from the work you're doing?" one of the guards asked. "Or anything that would be harmful to the Reich?"

"No," I replied and almost choked on the word.

Once outside the gate I ran quickly to the *Kindergarten*, picked up the children and hurried to the small room we shared with another family. The other occupants were not in so I took out the rag and unfolded it.

"Christ in heaven!" I said. "It's a map of our factory!" I slipped it back inside my trousers and sat down on the bed. "Why in hell did they pick me for this mission? I'm the biggest coward under the sun. Dear God, when will you stop punishing me? And what am I supposed to do with this thing?"

The door opened and a man came in. He was dressed in a laborer's uniform.

"You can give it to me," he said almost as if he had overheard me.

"Who are you?" I asked.

The man saw the fear in my face and smiled.

"One of you," he said gently. "You did us a great service."

I took out the rag and gave it to him. He stuffed it in his pocket like a handkerchief and left without another word.

▨   ▨   ▨

Not many days later I was at my machine when the lights started flickering. For the moment, the lights stayed on and the rhythm of the machines went back to normal. But then a tremendous shock caused the walls to sway. The glass partitions in a nearby office cracked. People started to run in different directions looking for cover. More shocks shook the building and the huge supporting beams cracked, then caved in with a horrifying roar.

I ducked under my machine and sat there. The lights went out and the building continued to crumble all around me. Hours passed. I heard the screams and moans of injured workers but I couldn't see a thing. Debris was still falling all around me and the concussion of exploding bombs kept shaking the ground.

"Dear Jesus, this is hell!" I said out loud. "Why am I still alive? I don't want to die slowly. You took the others, why not me? I can't breathe! I have no air to breathe!"

"Stay close to the floor," a man's voice said out of the darkness. "There's still some air left but only close to the ground. Don't get up or try to walk."

Time passed slowly and the bombing continued all day long. I began to worry about my children. If the bombs had managed to penetrate a factory that was meant to withstand bombardment, the entire camp above ground must be destroyed and all the people dead. It made me feel sick. Then the bombing stopped and deathly silence returned.

"Follow me," I heard the man say. "I'll keep talking so you can follow my voice."

I crawled slowly through the debris. I heard more voices and moans.

"Try not to touch anything," the man said. "If you disturb something it could collapse on you."

I crawled through the dark and the debris for a long time, hours perhaps. Time had no meaning. I heard drilling overhead and the ground started to shift. A muffled voice came from above.

"We're sending down oxygen tanks and ladders!"

"Hurry!" the man said.

I heard the tanks come down but couldn't reach them. I started to feel drowsy.

"Climb up this ladder," I heard the man tell someone. "Don't touch anything on either side or you'll bring it all down on us."

I waited a long time until my turn came.

"Now," a hand touched my head. "You're next."

I felt the rope in my hand and slowly stood up. I put my foot on the first rung of the ladder and started to climb, higher and higher. It was a long climb through a dark and narrow passage. Finally I saw lights high overhead. After a desperate struggle with my drowsiness I pulled myself above ground and was quickly grabbed by eager hands and lifted to safety.

"Dear God," I mumbled. "I feel like I helped kill all these people. Why didn't I die with them?"

I was taken to the mess hall which had somehow escaped destruction. By candle light I was given a cup of cold coffee and a slice of bread. I drank the coffee and chewed on the bread. Then I lay down on a bench in the corner and closed my eyes. I had almost fallen asleep when the shrill voice of a Russian woman roused me.

"My daughter was in the *Kindergarten*!" the woman lamented. "Now it's all gone and the children with it!"

I was instantly awake. I struggled to my feet and staggered outside. I looked around but could see nothing. Rain was starting to fall. There were no lights anywhere. I tried to walk but stumbled into fallen trees and smashed buildings. I fell to my knees and turned my face up into the sky. The rain hit me in the face and washed the tears away.

"My babies are dead!" I shouted angrily. "Oh God, when will you stop punishing us? When will you use your power to stop this atrocity? Never! You'll never hear us! You don't care! You don't exist! I don't believe in you!"

I found my way back to the mess hall and slumped into a corner. I fell asleep and for a time my body and heart were released from the horror and pain I had just lived through. When I opened my eyes I saw Jan standing over me.

"Jan!" I moaned with my last ounce of strength. "You're alive! My God, am I glad to see you!"

"Dear Jesus, I thought you were dead!" Jan said.

"I'm all right but my babies are dead," I said. "All the children are dead."

"No, ours are alive," Jan said. "All of them. I got them out of the *Kindergarten* when the bombs started to fall. We hid in a bomb crater."

My heart leaped with joy.

"Thank God they're alive!" I said. "Take me to them!"

Jan put his arms around me and helped me to my feet.

"And thank you, Jan, for saving our children and for caring about me," I added. "I always thought you hated me but maybe I was wrong."

Jan smiled.

"I don't blame you," he said. "I hurt you terribly and don't expect a pardon from you. I don't hate you and never did, but if you hate me, I understand."

"I don't know what I feel, Jan," I said. "I don't love you and I don't hate you. I'm just terribly happy and grateful to you that my babies are alive."

I kissed my husband warmly for the first time since I had known him, and somehow my hurt towards him diminished a bit.

Chapter Thirty-Three

The factory and the camp had been reduced to rubble. My family and I were among the survivors of that devastation. There were about fifteen hundred others, all of whom were being loaded onto a train.

"Not another train," I groaned. "I can't bear it. They're always taking us into the unknown."

My children were hungry and cold. Scabs covered their heads.

"We're rotting alive and nobody gives a damn," I said. "Not even God."

"At least we're alive," Jan said.

"But for how long? And where are they taking us now?"

Jan turned me around to face him.

"It has to end someday," he said. "We'll survive. I know we will."

I wanted to believe him. I took my place on the floor of the freight car and closed my eyes. I heard the door close and felt the train lurch forward. Soon we were rolling through the night.

When dawn came the train stopped and the door was flung open. It was a crisp sunny morning. The light hurt my eyes and I shielded them. I saw the figure of a woman walking along the ramp carrying a pail.

"Jan!" I shouted. "It's my mother!

"She's supposed to be in Austria," Jan said. "What would she be doing here?"

I stood up and waved. "Mother! Over here! It's me, Victoria!"

The woman turned her head to look. She gave a slight wave back and continued on her way.

"She didn't recognize me!" I said near tears.

One of the guards banged the butt of his rifle against the car.

"Inside! Shut up!" he yelled.

Jan pulled me away from the door.

"It was her!" I said. "I know it was her!"

A man in civilian clothes approached the train, followed by two uniformed policemen.

"This car!" the man said. "Everybody out!"

We hurried to obey. I handed the children down to Jan and jumped down myself. When the car was empty the whistle blew and the train moved on with the other survivors still aboard. We stood waiting on the ramp for further orders. The sign above us said we were in a town called Vacha.

"Now I'll be able to find out if that was really my mother," I whispered to Jan.

"Don't be ridiculous," he said. "It was just a coincidence."

We were taken to work in a factory with four hundred Polish slave laborers, producing parachutes. Life was much easier than it had been. For one thing, there were no bombs. Food was of poor quality but it was edible. And during the harvest we were allowed to help German farmers in return for better food.

Once again, I saw the woman who looked like my mother. I stared at her until I realized she really was Frances Paff! Overjoyed, I ran up to her and embraced her. We covered each other's faces with tearful kisses and Mother explained how their train to Vienna was bombed and in the confusion, she and the children were sent to work camp in Germany. When I learned that my brother and sister were also in Vacha my joy was almost complete. I began to think that maybe there was a God after all. It was tempered somewhat when I learned that my other brother and sister were still unaccounted for.

Jan, the children and I were given a private room. We no longer had to share our quarters with strangers. The barracks in which we lived was constructed of thin wooden planks. A cast iron stove provided enough heat in the fall, but winter found it wanting. The scanty firewood we found would not keep it lit. Snow blew through the cracks in the wall and the bucket of water froze solid every night.

With the coming of spring everybody's spirits lifted. Conditions had not changed but rumors were sweeping the camp that the Germans were losing the war. They were being beaten back on front after front. Secretly, everybody exulted.

But I was plagued by another worry. Poles were forbidden to marry and have children, and my swollen belly could no longer be hidden. The commandant of the factory called me into his office.

"You've broken the law and can be hanged for it," he said. "You can't give birth, so you'd better get rid of it. I don't care how."

I went back to our quarters and took out my fury on Jan.

"If I have the baby they'll hang me," I said. "But god-damit, you had as much to do with it as I did!"

"So what do you propose to do?" Jan asked.

"I'll have the baby in the woods and leave it there to die," I said. "Then I'll come back and kill you for all the trouble you've been."

Jan laughed. "Victoria, you couldn't kill a bug."

Throughout the remaining weeks of pregnancy I wavered between despair and hope. I tried to figure out how to have the baby and hide it from the Germans until the war was over but nothing seemed to make sense. Then, on the morning of April 25, I was awakened by cannon fire roaring over the barracks. Jan had already gone to work so I gathered the children together and huddled in a corner with them. Soon Jan came back and grabbed a shovel.

"We have to dig trenches," he said. "The Germans are on one side, shooting at tanks on the other side. We're caught in the middle!"

"My God, what kind of tanks?" I asked fearfully. "Russian?"

"American, I think."

Jan went back out and the deafening barrage continued. After a while he came back and escorted us into one of the freshly dug trenches. They were already filled with people.

"God help us," I prayed as I sheltered the children with my body. "We've lived through hell, and now that freedom's so near, please don't let us die!"

German soldiers suddenly appeared above the trench and trained their guns on us.

"Who are you?" one of them asked in a thundering voice.

"Workers from the factory," somebody answered.

"Get out! We need these trenches!"

The people filed out quickly, children crying, women shivering and weeping, men silent and ashen. We expected to be executed on the spot but the Germans ignored us and piled into the trenches as fast as we vacated them.

Horror stricken, we fled through the heavy underbrush as bullets and shrapnel swept the ground around us. Somebody fell but nobody stopped.

"My daughter!" I heard my mother scream.

I turned and saw my sister lying on the ground. I was about to go back when a young man stopped me and ran back for her. He picked her up and carried her to the shelter of a small hill. The explosive rattle of machine guns began again and everybody hugged the ground.

"Crawl to the salt mine!" somebody shouted. "We're in a crossfire!"

I couldn't crawl. My belly was too big. Crying and cursing Jan, I managed to slide along on my side.

"Take the children to the mine!" I called to Jan. "Leave me here!"

"Crawl, dammit!" he shouted. "Move!"

"I can't!" I sobbed. "Not anymore!"

There was anguish in Jan's eyes as he looked back at me.

"We'll never make it to the mine together," he said.

"Then save the children."

"No!" Jan said. "We can hide in the drain pipe under the tracks."

I didn't care where we went as long as I could rest. I let Jan help me into the drain pipe, and then he went back and got the children. As my eyes adjusted to the darkness I saw that the pipe was filled along its entire length with refugees. The explosions persisted and the ground shook, but at least the danger of being hit by shrapnel had diminished.

"Do you know what today is?" I asked Jan.

He shook his head.

"Holy Thursday," I said. "I wonder if we'll live to see Easter Sunday."

"Easter will come, Mommy," little Val said.

I caressed his tear-stained cheek.

"Yes Val, it will," I said. "We're going to make it."

The gunfire subsided about midnight. Numb, we slept. But early the next morning the shooting began again and the doors to hell truly opened. Exploding rounds filled the drain pipe with black acrid smoke, choking everybody inside. We didn't dare leave, not even to relieve ourselves.

The shooting continued through Good Friday, Holy Saturday, Easter Sunday and Monday. When finally it stopped, everybody was stunned by the sudden silence. We waited for something to happen. Nothing. Then we heard a man with a strange accent say something in German.

"Who are you?" he said. "Come out of there!"

I looked out of the drain pipe and into the barrel of a machine gun. It was held by a black man. I had never seen a black man before.

"Holy God!" I said. "This is the end!"

We crawled out of the pipe and stood before him with our hands folded behind our heads.

"What nationality are you?" the soldier asked, still in awkward German.

"Polish," Jan said. "We are Poles."

The soldier laughed. "Polka, polka!" he said.

Other soldiers came out of the smoke and gathered around us. One of them pointed at my enormous belly and grinned.

"Don't look at me!" I said. "Don't laugh! I'm tired!"

I could bear no more and slid to the ground unconscious. When I awoke, an army medic was kneeling beside me taking my pulse. The children were right there, devouring American chocolate, their faces smeared but smiling.

"Victoria, we're liberated!" Jan said. "We are free people! My God, we are free!"

The black soldier brought me some crackers and a canteen filled with orange juice. It tasted sweet, like nectar of the gods.

"May God bless you, American soldiers," I said. "May God bless you and your country."

When the medic felt my belly the baby inside kicked back furiously. It was as if he too knew we were finally free.

Epilogue

*I*n the village of Carynskie, they say the mountain is haunted. No one goes up there anymore, neither shepherd nor hunter. Those who dare go there say that a violent wind will suddenly roar through the tall pines with enough force to tear the trees out by their roots. But then the roar subsides to the whistling howl of a wailing woman calling her lover's name. Some have even seen a young woman running through the woods with her arms outstretched and her long black hair streaming behind her.

The trees in the forest grow taller and bigger with time. People come to the towns and villages in the Carpathian Mountains, live their lives and die. New generations take their place. Yet the mountains never change. They are the same solid towers they were in 1944. It is a fitting memorial that in these natural surroundings Sheila Landow's voice and spirit lives on. She tried to save so many lives, worked so hard in such difficult times, and at last was shot along with hundreds she attempted to deliver from the guns.

After the war, Edward Hertig returned to Lutowiska in search of Sheila. He found her house burned to the ground.

He picked up a piece of charcoal and kept it on a shelf in his home in Poland where I saw it when I visited him. He eventually married, had eleven children and died in 1993.

My lost brother was forced to return to Poland where he married and raised three children. We found him in the late fifties and helped him and his family move to the United States.

My lost sister turned up in a camp at the end of the war. She moved to the United States with my mother and the two youngest children. Mother died in 1991. All of her children have families of their own.

I still remember Ivan. And my husband Jan—well, he's old and says he loves me, but there are much more important things now.

My eldest son Mitchel lives in Illinois and works for a large insurance company. Next in line is Val, who lives on Long Island and works for a municipality. Adam lives on Long Island too, and works for a large advertising agency. Joseph, the youngest, lives in Washington State and works as a personnel manager for a major corporation. They have given me nine grandchildren.

These are my flowers, from whom joy is coming and healing my heart.